LANGDIMANIA

LACH

Copyright © Lach 2021

First edition published in the UK by

The Book Whisperers

Cover Art by David Schofield

Art Direction by Mary Turner Thomson and Lach

TABLE OF CONTENTS[1]

---

[1] Dear Reader - You'll find that this book contains extraordinary events including imaginary words, time distortions, floating people, and some very short chapters. It also has a, shall we say, uncluttered Table of Contents. Feel free to set the table any way you wish. Oh, it also has footnotes written by hand.

CHAPTER 1

One can never truly pinpoint where a story begins. You may say that it's the birth of the main character that sets the events in motion, but then wouldn't it be their parents' birth that actually starts the story? Or their grandparents' birth? Or their great-grandparents' birth and on and on, all the way back through time, to the very first amoeba dividing in the ocean to start the evolutionary climb towards land? Or even further to Earth's creation from spinning gas and dust or further still to the big bang? And what, and it's this thought that kept Army's head spinning, was there before the big bang?

Army's full name was Abraham Armstrong Allen, but just about everybody called him Army. He was an inquisitive and imaginative boy living in the suburbs of New York City. On his twelfth birthday, he visited a progressive toy store in Manhattan called 'Imagination at Play' and was allowed to pick out a few items for himself as presents. And that is how this story begins, after all, choices do have to be made or we'll never get anywhere in life, or so Army's mother would always say. Perhaps the big bang was simply the universe making a choice to exist.

If Army had made the choice to exist, to choose from the before-world of being born, he would have chosen a place and family way more exotic than the one he got. He always felt that he landed just south of his destination. Oh, he liked himself all right and he loved his family, but he never quite felt at home in his life. Looking in the mirror, the boy he saw reflected back looked normal enough. Dark brown hair, brown eyes, average height and weight, a bit slender perhaps, if anything. "Actually, rather good-looking!" he thought.

Army was not short of self-esteem or 'joie de vivre'. (That's French for 'joy of life'.) He was taking French in school and, as a result, had mastered three major things. First, how to lean back in his chair so that he was balancing on just the back legs without falling over. Secondly, how to get a crumpled-up piece of paper into a wastepaper basket from the other side of the room without his teacher, Mr Dumont, catching him. Thirdly, how to do both at the same time. As for learning any French? Well, not so much. In fact, Army had loads of 'vivre' but he just couldn't figure out why everyone else seemed to be in a deficit on that account. His older brother, Nick, for instance, spent most after-school afternoons by himself in his dark bedroom watching ballgames on an old television set. Army would have to bribe him with leftover Halloween treats just to get his older sibling to reluctantly join in a board game of *Risk* or *Life*; two games named after things Nick was normally devoid of otherwise. Army had memories of times before his brother turned into a cliché of the sullen teen so often portrayed on television sitcoms. The loss of that companionship was confusing but Army's parents described it as a "phase" his brother was going through and so he thought it best to avoid him until it passed like a long, drawn-out cold.

Army's dad was too busy with work, and his mom was too caught up with her pottery classes, book clubs, and lunches 'with the ladies', to join in the make-believe adventures that Army so longed to share with someone. And so, he'd spend his days exploring the woods behind his house or the local construction yards using his imagination to turn them into alien worlds or secret spy encampments.

Espionage was an art form Army had perfected. He rated his neighbors on their ability to spot him, assigning them different colors to designate how good they were at doing so. For instance, Mrs Caulfield, who lived three houses down from Army and seemed to be constantly putting clothes on the drying line, was a yellow. Army could practically stand smack dab in front of her and she wouldn't even notice, but Sonny, her German Shepherd, was a red and could sense Army before he had even made it out of his front door. Army's dog, Ginger, a shaggy mutt, part terrier, part some other kind of terrier was, on the other hand, a gentle creature, and though she was probably a yellow, Army bumped her rank up to orange. What Ginger lacked in Sonny's aggressive alertness she more than made up for in her ability to listen, not just for threats and falling food but to Army's thoughts on just about anything, and his feelings about everything.

Sometimes an angry newspaper boy or census taker would yell at Ginger after tripping over her on the way up to the Allen's front door and mutter, "Dumb animal." But Army knew that even though Ginger couldn't talk (and Army really wished that she could), she was a very smart animal indeed.

"You and me girl," Army would whisper to Ginger after confiding to her about his loneliness, "no one else understands."

And Ginger would lick his face like she understood even if no one else did.

Army loved making believe and one of his favorite fantasies was that he was exploring a distant planet and that his neighbors were alien military out to capture him. Airplanes flying overhead became, in Army's imagined world, advanced scout drones sent to find and take him in as a prisoner of a never-ending intergalactic war. He'd make-believe that he could shoot the aircraft down by pointing his index finger at the jet and then directing his thumb at an angle away from him. This technique would fool the otherworldly authorities into believing that his laser fire came from the distant spot his thumb indicated, thus leaving him time to make his getaway.

Another ruse he perpetrated was the frozen statue trick. It seemed that the police, on the planet that Army imagined he was a fugitive on, used statues as their equivalent of wanted posters. How naive! When they'd get too close to Army he'd simply freeze and trick them into thinking he was a wanted statue of himself. The fools never suspected a thing! However, an errant mosquito on a hot summer day could prove disastrous and more than one bite was endured so as not to give himself away to the oddly chuckling Mrs Caulfield.

Now, where were we? Oh yes, Army was exploring the shelves at 'Imagination at Play' from top to bottom looking for the perfect present to choose for his last birthday before becoming a teenager. He already had enough toy cars to start his own dealership. He had loads of Legos, pails of puzzles, bags of bouncing balls, and piles of puppets. He was losing hope of ever finding anything when he saw, from out of the corner of his eye, a bird flying in the store. Not a toy bird but a big, black crow! Uncertain if he actually saw it, Army rubbed his eyes only to open them again to see the bird drop something out of its mouth into a silver, wire basket standing on the store's floor and then fly away out of the shop's window.

Army looked about the store to see if anyone else saw what he had witnessed but everyone was simply going about their business as if nothing had happened. Army cautiously approached the metal hamper to find that it contained a slew of strange, plastic spheres of various colors; red, yellow and blue. They were dotted with protruding buttons, like mini Sputnik satellites that could fit into the palm of your hand. Army quickly forgot about the bird as the objects in the basket fascinated him. He found that he could depress any of the knobs into the toy and they'd quickly pop back out again. It was the simplest of playthings, but quite often those are the best. The imagination is infinite, and without the limitations imposed by game rules or gadget manuals this object, which according to a sign hanging from the basket was called Thingamajig, could do *anything*.

Army selected a blue one which, for some reason, seemed to call out to him, and he spent endless hours over the following weeks fiddling with the buttons while imagining all sorts of things they could make happen. He made believe that he turned Ginger into a Stegosaurus using the Thingamajig's devo beam and together they conquered the zombie cavemen of Trikalison. The people of the distant planet Oragio declared him a cosmic saint when he

5

inoculated their crops from a killer plant disease using the gleaming blue sphere's anti-bacterial Z-ray! The Thingamajig gave Army the added powers of flight, invisibility, and invulnerability during his afterschool adventures. He'd go to bed at night creating new stories about his toy as he drifted off to sleep, and he kept the Thingamajig resting on a shelf just above his head so that he could see it first thing in the morning when he awoke.

CHAPTER 2

O ne early autumn morning on the bus to school, Army's Thingamajig fell out of his pocket and into the lap of Willie Mueller, the slight, blonde-haired boy sitting next to him. Willie picked up the toy and stared at it in wonder.

"Give it back," Army said. "It's mine."

"What is it?" Willie asked.

"Never mind what it is. Just give it back to me quick!" Army said, his voice rising in feigned panic. "It can blow us all up!"

The boy cautiously passed the toy back to his classmate, his eyes wide in curiosity. "But what is it exactly?" he repeated. "What does it do?"

"It does everything," Army whispered mysteriously.

"Like what?"

"Well, for instance, it keeps all of reality in motion," Army improvised.

"Huh? What do you mean?"

"Nothing in the world exists until this magic ball wills it to exist," Army said, enjoying his chance to finally give voice to his imagined powers.

"Oh, get out of here," Willie said dismissively.

"Yeah? Then how do you explain everything that's here, that's around us? Me, you, the school bus, the road?"

"That's easy," Willie said with a smug smile. "God created everything."

"And who," Army said, pausing dramatically, "made God?"

The boy blinked at Army, bewildered by the most basic of arguments. The bus stopped to pick up some more kids going to school. Army used the opportunity of the new passengers filing past him to casually look towards the back of the bus and sneak a glimpse of Wendy, the girl whose smile made Army's world light up. Just knowing that he was on the same bus as her made Army's heart race. He wasn't even sure why. Yes, she was pretty with dark raven hair and sparkling hazel eyes, but it was more than that. It was like she was a part of him; a part he didn't fully understand, but he felt that she could explain.

"I don't know, who?" Willie stammered.

"Who what?" Army replied, having lost the thread of their conversation.

"Who made God?"

"Not who, Willie, but what," Army said, turning back around and indicating the ball cradled in his hand. "This. It can create anything!"

"Yeah, right, and pigs have wings," Willie retorted. They rode along for a bit in silence until Willie couldn't take it anymore and asked, "How come *you* have it?"

Army was amazed that the conversation had gone this far. He had Willie going all right. "Because I'm not really from here," Army said in a conspiratorial tone. "I'm from the time and dimension before things ever existed, and I use this to help me do my job of bringing things into reality."

"But what is it? What's it called?"

In a flash of inspiration, or more like he was remembering something that he never knew he had forgotten, Army replied that it was a Langdim Finder. He explained that 'Langdim' was short for language and dimension, and that the little, plastic blue ball could transport him to other dimensions and help him understand the various languages the inhabitants of those alternative worlds spoke.

Luckily, before Willie could ask Army to actually speak in another reality's language, the bus had pulled into the school parking lot and they joined the mad rush to morning classes.

CHAPTER 3

A ll that day, Army was enamored with what was once a Thingamajig but was now a Langdim Finder, and he fantasized a scenario where he was the king of another dimension he dubbed Langdimania. He drew elaborate maps of the place and declared it to be the Eighteenth Dimension[2]. In addition, Army's Langdimanian name turned out, to his delight, to be the same as his favorite fighter plane, the Spitfire, and he began to draw the letters LSF all over his notebooks and eventually the desks throughout the school building. LSF was short for Langdimania and Spitfire Forever. Obviously.

In his wood working class, Army carved the letters L, S, and F out of individual blocks of pine. He gave the S to his best school friend Mike and the F to Mike's current girlfriend Debbie, keeping the L for himself. He filled them in on his inter-dimensional royal status and they enjoyed

---

[2] It actually was a bit more complicated than that; Army's daydreams usually were. He decided that the third dimension, the one we're all used to, had infinite offshoots (alternate universes if you will) and that Langdimania was the eighteenth of these. So, in reality (reality being whatever Army decided to dream about from one moment to the next instead of listening to his teachers' lectures) Langdimania wasn't the eighteenth dimension but, technically speaking, it was actually the 3^{18} dimension. Army felt distinctions like these helped give his theories more heft.

being inducted into the secret. It also provided them with a topic of conversation beyond trying to figure out where in the school they could sneak off to together or how to get a ride to the local mall.

The next day in school, Mike and Debbie approached Army to settle an argument over who was his second in command. It hadn't occurred to Army that this would become an issue. To keep the peace, he made Debbie his immediate underling, Mike hers, and told them that the next day, they would switch ranks but that he, Army, would always be top ranked because, after all, he was the king of Langdimania. They had a blast and every once in a while Army would pass one of them a note with a mission they'd have to carry out, such as stealing the toilet pass from the teacher's desk.

Word started going around the school about what Army and his friends were up to and, when the other kids heard about this, let's be frank, rather romantically-tinged game going on, well, they wanted in on it too! By the end of the week, Army had about a dozen couples initiated into the imperial role-playing game at various ranks. It evolved into a sort of chain letter taking on a life of its own. It was an irresistibly easy plan to enact; Army would simply approach a kid in the playground and ask him or her if they'd like their own servant for a day.

"What do you mean?" they'd ask with an apprehensive look.

"Well, someone to get your school milk or do your homework for you," Army would reply.

Their eyes would light up with the possibilities and they'd warily inquire, "What would I have to do?"

At this point, Army knew he had them. "It's simple," he'd say. "All you have to do is be someone else's servant for just one day, and then you'll get your own servant for two days!"

After they'd agreed, he'd then go up to the next kid and offer the same deal only increasing the term by a day. Or he'd mix it up so the person that was owed three days of being waited upon would get a new servant each day from the growing pool of acolytes. Army always made sure to explain that he, as the organizer of the whole thing, would be ruler over them all.

It was complete madness. It spread like wildfire, as no kid wanted to be left out of the game. He had to devise an elaborate system of royal titles to work out who was beholden to whom. There were so many! Even limiting himself to the British titles that he understood the best (so no Emperors, Czars or Chieftains) he still had to parse his way through Princes and Princesses, Dukes and Duchesses, Marquises and Marchionesses, Earls and Countesses, Viscounts and Viscountesses, Barons and Baronesses, Knights, Dames, and Lords and Ladies! It took some complex calculations on Army's part, eventually creating elaborate lists and charts to keep track of everything, but pretty soon he had a list of over one hundred students all in royal service to each other. They were running around the school delivering each other's lunches, shining shoes and being lookouts for teachers. There were Earls bowing to Dukes, Baronesses curtsying before Princes, and Knights saluting everybody, which was much appreciated by the school custodian. Army was kept busy arbitrating boyfriend/girlfriend arguments over which one was in charge of the other on any particular day.

And somehow, unaffected by it all, Wendy continued to float through the school, Army's daydream queen. That was the answer! She was already the queen of Langdimania in Army's daydreams; why not make it a reality? Who could resist such a proposition?

So, one night, after the nobility chain letter had been in operation for a few weeks, Army remade his pyramid list of teenage thralls into an exotic scroll to present to Wendy after school. He hardly slept that night knowing that the next day he would win her heart by presenting her the list and allowing her to rule by his side!

The next day went by in a blur as Army resolved several imperial disputes and picked up his physics homework from a studious serf named Ted. Army barely cared when his physical education contingent carried him into gymnastics class on their shoulders as if he were the pharaoh arriving to court. As they stood at attention in their gym uniforms he indulgently gave the onlookers the half-turn wave common to all royalty until the school coach blew his whistle and yelled for everyone to, "Cut it out!"

All that Army cared about that afternoon was for the school bell to ring, its shrill howl announcing the end of the day and signaling everyone to load onto the yellow and black school buses lined up to take them home. He was planning to present the scroll to Wendy then and to endow her with her own kingdom of loyal subjects. He was sure after such a gift she would be his.

However, unbeknownst to Army, Wendy had found out during the day about the pre-teen monarchy operating in the old brick school building. She'd discovered that half of her fellow classmates were going about the place madly barking orders at each other while the other half carried out their wishes.

"What in the world is going on?" she thought. "Who is responsible for this awful craziness?"

It didn't take long for Wendy to get the answers to her questions and as Army sat on the school bus waiting with delightful anticipation for her arrival, she was storming out of the school's front doors with angry fire in her eyes. Onto the bus she came, straight for Army.

"Is it true?" she confronted Army as the bus pulled away from the curb.

She found out! She already knew! But Army erroneously thought that Wendy knew in a good way. He thought the irate glow surrounding her was the aura of love and adoration. He couldn't have been more mistaken.

"Have you really convinced our class to take turns ruling over each other?" Wendy continued.

"See?" thought Army. "She's amazed. She's in awe!" Then gushing out loud he said, "Yes! Servants galore! And they are all yours!" And with a great flourish he bowed and handed her the scroll.

"What is this supposed to be?" Wendy asked.

"It's the Royalty Register of Langdimania. I am giving it to you. They all belong to you now, my queen!" Army beamed.

Wendy scrunched up her face as it turned a bright red.

"Are you KIDDING me?" she shouted. "Are you INSANE?"

It finally began to dawn on Army that perhaps his plan had a flaw in it.

"This is the sickest thing I have ever heard of in my life!" Wendy yelled at Army as she vigorously ripped the paper and his heart into shreds. She stamped down the bus aisle and left Army bewildered, broken, and ashamed. Those on the bus under Army's command attended to him in hushed tones assuring him that it would all be okay. But Army was inconsolable. The shine had wilted off of the rose of autocratic power. Feudalism had lost its charm.

The next day Army sent word that he was no longer in the aristocratic business of domination. Shortly afterwards, Mike and Debbie broke up, the game really being all that was holding the fickle nature of their romance together. Army decided he would still be the king of Langdimania, but only in his dreams from now on, no longer in the earthly dimension. That is until the following Tuesday when the weird thing happened in French class.

CHAPTER 4

Tuesdays were not Army's favorite days. A lot of his classmates complained about having the 'Monday Blues' from not wanting to go back to school after the weekend's freedoms. But for Army it was Tuesdays that were the drag. Even though school wasn't his favorite place in the world, he always felt a bit excited to go back in on Mondays. Up until this past week he had looked forward to seeing Wendy again in the hallways, and he enjoyed doing experiments in his science classes and writing strange stories about his after-school exploits in his English class. And now he always had The Langdim Finder at hand in his sweatshirt pocket to distract him from the monotony of school and to smooth out his afternoons with daydream adventures. But on Tuesdays, Army had French class which meant fifty minutes of the incredibly boring Mr Dumont. Truly, Mr Dumont had to be the most tedious teacher ever. Even The Langdim Finder couldn't battle against it.

Boring is boring enough in English but it's even worse in a language you don't understand. Army tried playing various games to keep awake, such as counting how many times Mr Dumont blinked and then recording each blink with a push of a Langdim button (the record was 738 times in fifty minutes). Or marking down how many times the wart on the inside of Mr Dumont's right upper arm made an appearance from beneath the short-sleeved shirts he'd wear to class (the record for this was 17).

The foreign language teacher was notorious for droning on and on in French until half of the class were reaching alpha states in surreptitious napping positions. They'd be hiding behind their propped-up language books and then, without warning, Mr Dumont would slam his yardstick down hard on an unsuspecting and dreaming student's desk while shouting, "Vous pouvez dormir quand vous êtes mort!"

As the student popped up, ears ringing, eyes blinking wildly, and gasping for air like a goldfish suddenly splashed out of the bowl, Mr Dumont would add, "Et vous le serez si vous ne faites pas attention!"

The school nurse, Mrs Healey, treated at least four or five cases of sore necks a year from students experiencing whiplash at the alarming whack of Mr Dumont's ruler.

On this particular Tuesday, a little less than a week after Wendy had torn Army's heart apart, Mr Dumont seemed to have decided on a radically different teaching method than his usual one of 'Total French Immersion' or TFI; the strategy of never allowing anything other than French to be spoken in the room. TFI drove Army crazy. How could you ask what a word meant or, even worse, understand the explanation of a word you don't know if it's only taught to you in a language you don't understand to begin with? (Probably by doing the assigned readings and homework, but how could that compete with Army's mission to settle the civil war on Omnicron Six?)

However, today, as Army entered the room while absentmindedly fiddling with The Langdim Finder in his pocket, Mr Dumont greeted his class using English, "Good morning boys and girls."

"That's odd," thought Army as he took his seat. "Why didn't Mr Dumont start things off by saying, 'Bonjour les garçons et les filles' like always?"

Mr Dumont moved from behind his teacher's desk and, turning to the chalkboard, he wrote what looked like to Army to be two sentences in, again of all things, English. Then, continuing in English, the instructor said to the class, "Who can tell me what this says?"

Army was confused. This *was* Mr Dumont's TFI French class wasn't it? Third period just before lunch? He looked around the room. His classmates sat at their desks looking up at the sentences on the chalkboard. He looked back at Mr Dumont who was wearing his usual short-sleeved shirt, this time a pale blue color, and, as always, there was the wart on his arm just barely visible beneath the fabric. Everything but the words on the board being in English was normal.

Mr Dumont saw Army looking bewildered and pounced on the opportunity to get him into hot water. He had a special dislike of Army who was constantly leaning back in his chair and distracting the other students. It was disrespectful, and he'd just as soon have the boy drop out or transfer to Spanish class.

"Let him be Miss Albarez's problem," Mr Dumont thought, as he called on Army to read the two French sentences he had written on the board.

Army was trying to figure out if he was the victim of a cruel prank by Mr Dumont. Why had the teacher written the usual morning sentences in English instead of French? It just didn't make sense.

"Is this some kind of joke?" Army exclaimed.

The class laughed. Army put his hand in his pocket and gripped The Langdim Finder for comfort.

"In French! In French!" cried Mr Dumont his face red with anger. "This is not a joke, young man; you are the joke! Now read these two sentences or I will give you a failing grade!"

Why was Mr Dumont yelling at him in English? Army started to sweat and began fiddling with The Langdim Finder in his pocket. Why were the morning sentences in English? And, most importantly, was he supposed to recite the sentences now in English as he thought they were written or translate them back into French?

Army gulped, pressed one of the buttons on his toy and looked at the board. It read, 'Can I please have another piece of melon?' and 'Would you like more tea?'

"I am in no way good enough to translate English into French. I'm much better at translating from French to English," anguished Army who was now pressing various buttons on his Langdim Finder and praying for a miracle. He looked at Mr Dumont shaking with irritation. "Well," Army thought, "if I'm going to go out, I might as well go out in style!"

And turning back to read from the board Army pressed three buttons at once and said aloud, "Est-ce que je peux avoir un autre morceau de melon? Voudriez-vous plus de thé?" ('Can I please have another piece of melon?' and 'Would you like more tea?') And then he added all on his own, full of revolutionary zeal and excitement at how easily the translation was coming to him, "Non merci, en fait, laisse tomber le thé et le melon, je prendrais un morceau de

19

gâteau!" ('No thank you. In fact, never mind the tea and melon, let me eat cake!')

Perfect French! He said it in perfect French! The class roared with laughter. "Army est mon héros! Hourra pour Army!" they shouted.

Mr Dumont sputtered, "Out! Out!" at Army in English and then caught himself and continued in French, "Sortez de la pièce! Sortez de ma classe! Se présenter au bureau du directeur immédiatement!"

Which Army automatically heard as, "Get out of the room! Get out of my class! Report to the principal's office immediately!"

Army walked head held high to the door, but before leaving he turned to address his class and quoting Napoleon bidding farewell to his old guard he announced, "Adieu, mes enfants! Je voudrais vous presser tous sur mon coeur!" ('Farewell, my friends. Would that I could press you all to my heart!')

Army saluted his cheering classmates and, with a flip of his sweatshirt hood, he marched out the door.

CHAPTER 5

This wasn't Army's first trip to the principal's office. There was that time he accidentally locked Donald Wilson in his school locker, the time he was found standing like a statue in the faculty lounge as a bewildered teacher, Mrs Kennedy, returned to pick up the test papers she had forgotten and, of course, the time he was exposed as the ringleader of a certain indentured Ponzi scheme. But this time it was different. This time on his way to the principal's office Army didn't have the usual feeling of dread accompanied by fantasies of life as a pre-teen drifter riding the trains heading west. No, this time he was too bewildered by what had just occurred in Mr Dumont's French class to entertain any fear of authoritarian retribution.

He kept going over it all while idly pressing The Langdim Finder's buttons as he slowly walked the empty school hallways on his way to Mr Finch's office.

"Now, let's see," Army said to himself. "The sentences on the board are usually in French but today they were in English and Mr Dumont was speaking English but insisting I speak in French. Why? And how did I speak perfect French when I had no idea what I was supposed to say? Where on Earth did 'je prendrais un morceau de gâteau!'

come from? I mean, I was thinking it'd be funny to do a takeoff on Marie Antoinette but how did I know how to do it?"

As Army was debating with himself he approached the open doorway of another classroom. He could hear the teacher reciting, "The dog is on the chair."

And then the class responding, "The dog is on the chair."

Army peeked in as he walked by and saw it was Miss Albarez's Spanish class.

"The dog is under the chair," Miss Albarez exclaimed.

"The dog is under the chair," The class responded.

"That's odd," Army thought. "I heard that Miss Albarez's class was also total immersion. Why aren't they speaking Spanish?"

At that moment Miss Albarez looked up and saw Army standing in the doorway looking in.

"Ah," she announced to her class, "it's the Army marching to the principal's office again I would assume."

The class laughed, and Army felt his face flush. He couldn't help himself and once again fidgeting with the buttons on The Langdim Finder, he shouted back at her in, amazingly enough, Spanish, "¿Puedo evitarlo si soy más inteligente que ustedes maestros?" (Can I help it if I'm smarter than you teachers?)

Miss Albarez blinked at him as a few of her students said, "Ooooh!"

"Army!" Miss Albarez cried out.

"Gosh," he thought to himself as he ran away, "I'm in enough trouble as it is. Why'd I have to do that? And since when do I know Spanish?"

Army arrived at the principal's office a bit out of breath and took a moment to compose himself.

"Well, there's nothing to do but get it over with," he thought, standing in front of Mr Finch's office door. "I mean, how much trouble could I be in for actually knowing my French for once? C'est très ironique! What'd I say? 'It is very ironic.' WHAT?"

Realizing he just had a thought in French and then translated it into English, Army felt his face flush again. Realizing his face was now turning red, Army started to sweat. Realizing his face was red and he was sweating, Army's hands began to shake. Of course, it was at that moment that the door to Mr Finch's office opened and there stood the principal's secretary, Mrs Alison.

"Here it comes," thought Army. "If she calls me Army I'm in the clear but if she goes all formal with the full-on three name greeting, I'm a cooked goose."

"Abraham Armstrong Allen!" Mrs Alison bellowed.

"Honk, honk!" Army replied, figuring in for a penny in for a pound!

CHAPTER 6

Mr Finch was a serious man. There was something almost military about him. He kept his silver-grey hair in a severe crew cut and always wore light gray trousers and a pastel colored shirt like a navy man on leave. He was of average height and weight, but solid in construction. He was the type of man who would stand strong against the wind instead of going with its flow. He did not like any disruptions to the order of the day, and here stood the boy who seemed to make it his mission in life to bring chaos to any routine.

"So, Abraham, here you are again," proclaimed Mr Finch. "What is it this time? Using the flagpole as a pirate ship's crow's nest? Posting a 'Stegosaurus tooth for sale' sign on the school bulletin board? Sneaking into the cafeteria to, how did you put it, 'debacterialize the food with your Z-ray'?"

"He also called me Abraham," thought Army to himself, "I'm really in for it this time."

"Oh no, it couldn't be any of those things," Mr Finch said, his voice rising in frustration, "because you've already done them!"

From behind his impeccably neat and organized desk, Mr Finch stared at Army. And stared.

And stared.

"What am I supposed to do?" thought Army staring back. "Is he expecting an answer?"

Finally, Mr Finch continued, "I've had a communication from Mr Dumont, your French teacher."

"A communication?" Army remarked to himself. "Why can't he just say a phone call?"

"He says you've been disrespectful and disruptive in class."

"Oh no," thought Army once again nervously pressing the buttons on his sphere, "the two 'disses'. Disrespectful and disruptive. The worst crimes one could commit in Mr Finch's world!"

"What do you have to say for yourself, Abraham? And stop fidgeting, hands out of your pockets!"

Army put his hands to his sides in dismay, however his mood lifted a bit as he realized that his previous experiences in this room gave him an advantage. He knew that as much as Mr Finch hated disrespect and disruption, he loved "initiative". He'd go on and on at school assemblies about how students should strive to show more of it.

"I was just trying to show some initiative, sir!" barked Army trying to sound like a good cadet.

"By mocking your teacher?" countered Mr Finch.

"No sir, by doing extra work. I got the morning sentences right and then added more to show initiative."

"Well, according to your teacher, the 'more' you added was not appreciated and was obviously premeditated."

"Pre-medic what, sir?"

"Premeditated. It means you had planned this little charade in advance with malice aforethought."

"A four what sir?" blinked Army.

"Aforethought! Meaning beforehand in jurisprudence," Mr Finch irritably replied.

"Jurassic what sir?"

"That's it!" Mr Finch exploded. "A week's detention will teach you some manners!"

A week's detention! That meant sitting in the detention room with musty smelling Mrs Czernowski the school's choir teacher instead of going outside for recess. Army had to confess, and by 'confess' I mean lie.

"But Mr Finch," cried Army, "it's just that from our past talks I've been working really hard on, as you say, applying myself. I've been working day and night on improving my French and I can speak and understand it perfectly now. Really! In fact, it's okay if Mr Dumont doesn't want me in class anymore. I don't need it."

Mr Finch looked at Army. Poor child, so easily checkmated.

"Go on then," the principal said.

"What?" asked Army.

"Tell me something in French," Mr Finch growled triumphantly.

"Easy peasy," thought Army, figuring that even if worse came to worse, Mr Finch wouldn't understand anyway. He absentmindedly put his hand back into his pocket to grip The Langdim Finder for security.

"And it'd better be good," the principal continued. "I'm fluent in three languages and French is one of them. Now, take your hand out of your pocket, stand up straight, and recite to me in French!"

"Terrific," thought Army. "Isn't this just perfect?"

And that thought was followed by another one, wondering just what he should say. He thought he'd say, "I speak French like a French man now, so can I use third period as free time?" But he thought it in English. What was the French for that? Army searched his mind for the correct phrase in French like one would search a messy bedroom for a lost sweet. What had happened to his newfound ability?

"Well… Abraham?" Mr Finch cajoled, and he stretched out Army's first name; coldly and acidly emphasizing each syllable like this: "Abe… Rah… Hammmm?"

"Uh… um… Je parle français…" Army stammered.

"Yes, yes, don't take all day!" Mr Finch interjected.

Army had no idea what he was saying but he thought perhaps if he just got started the right words would come out just like they did in Mr Dumont's class.

"Je parle français en France donc je suis trois fois libre et nu!" Army finally blurted out. He then smiled in satisfaction. "That'll show him!" he thought.

"Really, Abraham? You just told me that you speak French in France and thus you are three times naked and free. Is that true?" Mr Finch asked, with a look on his face that was part stern disapproval and part victorious sneer.

"Oh my god!" Army replied. "Is that what I said?"

Just then the school bell rang signaling lunchtime and recess.

"That's the bell," Mr Finch announced, "off to detention with Mrs Czernowski for you, young man, and I don't want to hear another word about Abraham Armstrong Allen unless it's that he's finally graduated our beloved school and moved on!"

CHAPTER 7

Mrs Czernowski was a big, matronly woman in her early sixties who kept her grey hair pulled back in a tight bun. She wore faded floral dresses and always propped her shell-frame eyeglasses halfway down her nose so that she could look over them and straight at you; giving the effect that she never believed what you were telling her was the complete truth. She was the ultimate detention teacher, uncomfortable to be around and impossible to fool. To top things off she emanated a pungent smell that was an unfortunate mix of mothballs, sausages, and wet wool socks.

When Army arrived in the detention room he was disappointed to find that he was the only student there. What? No one else got in trouble today? He wished he still had his servants so that he could make a few take detention with him in order to keep him company and more importantly, to keep the attention of Mrs Czernowski off of him.

"Hello Abraham," Mrs Czernowski said. "Come on in and have a seat."

Army headed to the back row of chairs to be in his own breathable world as much as possible.

"Not all the way back there, Mr Allen," Mrs Czernowski grinned. "Up in front. With me."

Army reluctantly slunked[3] up the aisle of desks and started to sit at the one furthest from the center of the room where his chaperone squatted.

"Not all the way over there. Over here, Abraham. Right here in front of me where I can keep my eye on you."

Army even more reluctantly and even more slunkily shuffled to the desk in front of Mrs Czernowski. Her overpowering emanations wafted over him, traveling up his nose like unbathed mountain climbers. As he settled into his seat he could feel her odor beginning to embed itself in his eyes, skin, and hair. He put his right hand into his right sweatshirt pocket, gripped his Langdim Finder and began pushing the buttons while picturing that he was activating an anti-odor oxygen mask and HAZMAT suit.

Army let out a sound imitating the imagined hiss of a helmet sealing him into a Mrs Czernowski-free fantasy world, "Puh-shishsssss."

Army blinked.

What was happening to the fluorescent lights? They were suddenly turning rapidly off and on in a strobe effect. He sat straight up and looked at Mrs Czernowski, but she wasn't there. In fact, the room wasn't there anymore either! Army found himself sitting in an open field under a sky that

---

[3] Yes, I know, 'slunked' is not a 'real' word. But many words weren't real words until everyone began using them. As the writer of this book, I'll be using my own words for some things and eventually you'll see that they'll become just as real as any other words you may know. See if you can tell which words I invented and maybe one day you'll invent new words too!

was switching back and forth between the bright blue of day and dark black of night.

"What's going on?" Army cried out loud. He looked around in a panic as if he was falling from a great height. Was that a castle at the edge of the field? He jumped to his feet, let go of The Langdim Finder, took his hands out of his pockets and waved them in front of his face in an instinctive act of protection. Suddenly, the flashing stopped and he was back in the detention room, arms wildly flailing in the air as Mrs Czernowski stared at him, her eyes insanely enlarged by her glasses, making her look like a giant, bemused frog.

"Is that the new dance craze, young man? Because, honestly, I've got to tell you, it's really not that good."

CHAPTER 8

Vladimir wasn't the smartest animal in the world, but he certainly wasn't the dumbest either. When the dark/light moments happened, he immediately realized that The Arrival was imminent. He happened to be at his desk[4] in the stone Science Tower studying the latest patterns (Vladimir was the top Patternologist in the land) when the phenomenon occurred. His first reaction was to glance over at the light orbs in the walls to see if perhaps the crystals had worn out, but he quickly surmised that the odds of all of them needing regenerating at the same time were near infinite. Of course, being who he was, this thought was immediately followed by another one which Vladimir had had before and it had always greatly disturbed him, which was this, "How can something be near infinite if infinity has no end? Can a distance away from infinite actually be calculated?" These kinds of thoughts tended to make Vladimir dizzy and that, combined with the strobing

---

[4] Vladimir's desk was a wondrous thing befitting a creature of his station:.a grandly ornate oak table that sat in the center of the circular room upon a raised platform. It was chaotically covered with all sorts of papers, glass spheres, large well-used candles that had dripped wax like stalactites down their brass candle holders, ancient scrolls, inkwells and quills, charts, maps, and strange objects.

light, caused him to stagger on his hooves over to the window for air. Hooves? Oh yes, did I forget to mention it? Vladimir is a pig. A pig that can stand upright, is fond of wearing tartan waistcoats (today his vest was bedecked in a red and black checker pattern) with black trousers, and he often has a pair of gold-rimmed, round reading glasses propped upon his snout[5].

Vladimir pushed the window open and with closed eyes to minimize the effect of the flashing lights, he took a deep snort of fresh air cooled by the autumn winds. "With just a touch of that silvery taste of winter's coming," he thought to himself.

Then his ears went into full alert, standing straight up mode. Something more than the bizarre flickering had caught his attention. A smell. Pigs in general, and Vladimir in particular, have a keen sense of smell and he was smelling a smell he had never smelled before. Sort of like a piglet, but mustier, more piquant; a touch of basil mixed with a pinch of a sheep that's been left out in the rain. What could it be? He opened his eyes and peered out into the flickering distance of the castle's gardens and fields and though his eyesight was nowhere near that of his olfactory prowess, he thought he saw, for just a moment before disappearing, an extraordinary creature hopping up and down, waving its arms and doing the strangest of dances.

---

[5] Vladimir is the sole animal in this story that wears clothes. The other animals that you will meet along the way forgive him this bizarre idiosyncrasy as he is the High Patternologist and such a job often results in eccentric behaviors.

CHAPTER 9

A rmy fell back into his chair bewildered and dazed. What just happened? One second he was making believe he was putting on a protective suit and helmet and the next second he was standing in an open field and now he was back again. Was that a castle he saw?

"Well, Army, if this is your latest trick to get out of detention, I'm afraid it won't work. Though it is different, I must admit," said Mrs Czernowski.

"Trick?" said Army. "You think I caused all that?"

"Caused all what? What are you talking about?" his chaperone said with a look of concern on her face.

"The lights... the... the room disappearing... the castle!" Army cried.

"Oj bóg chłopak szaleje," Mrs Czernowski muttered under her breath in her native Polish.

"What?" Army asked in a panic, thinking his hearing was now going haywire as well. He shoved his hand into his pocket and once again began nervously pressing buttons on The Langdim Finder.

"Nothing, Army," the teacher continued. "I just remembered I needed to call my, um, sister. Excuse me for a second. Just relax while I make this call." And with that she got up from her desk and hurried outside into the hallway.

Army arose as well. He was now on high alert and suspicious of everything. He sneaked over to the partly opened classroom door where he could clearly hear Mrs Czernowski speaking into her phone in her native tongue. At first, Army didn't understand as he heard her say, "Martwię się o chłopca."

Excitedly fiddling with The Langdim Finder, Army leaned in closer in order to eavesdrop better and then, like tuning in an old radio from static to a clear channel he heard Mrs Czernowski's Polish transform into English mid-sentence, "… chłopiec boy. I think he may need a psychiatrist!"

"She thinks I'm crazy!" Army thought to himself in alarm.

Mrs Czernowski continued on, "Either that or else the boy's on drugs he shouldn't be on, or he's off the ones he's supposed to be on."

"That's insane," Army thought. "She thinks I'm insane. Am I insane?"

"Yes, yes…" Mrs Czernowski continued into the phone, "I'll keep him occupied until you get here, Mr Finch."

Mr Finch! On no, this was the worst. She wasn't really talking to her sister but instead she was telling on him to the principal! Mr Finch had already said he didn't want any more problems from Army. Where do they send you if you've failed at detention? Do they ship you off to jail? Or maybe, after what he had overheard, the insane asylum!

"I've got get out of here!" thought Army, pressing madly at The Langdim Finder's buttons. Simultaneously, the lights started to go wacky again and once more Army saw the room around him blink out of existence to be replaced with the open field.

"Oh my god," Army said out loud in astonishment, "It's happened again. Maybe I *am* crazy!"

"Or maybe you are The Arrival I've been waiting for," chimed in Vladimir who had been exploring the field to see where the dancing creature had disappeared to.

"A pig!" Army uttered in shock. "A talking pig!"

"Well, of course I talk. What a strange thing to say. Oop, I think he's passing out…"

CHAPTER 10

When Army awoke he was lying on a red velvet couch trimmed with gold embroidery in a circular room made of smooth, rounded stones. His right cheek felt wet and looking up into the distance he saw that the walls of the room rose high above his head, ending in a large domed skylight. The walls themselves housed illuminated spheres scattered about in a seemingly random design, lending the room a beautiful light that seemed to both energize and relax. Army felt as if he was at the base of a giant kaleidoscope.

"Feeling better?" a faintly familiar voiced asked Army.

Army looked behind him only to see Vladimir staring at him with his big blue eyes and then he passed out again, his hand falling out of his pocket, off of the couch, and on to the floor.

"Oh dear," Vladimir said, and once again he began poking the boy on his cheek with his long wet snout. "Wake up, do wake up!"

Just then there was a tapping at the window that Vladimir had shut when he had gone out into the field to investigate. The pig looked over and saw his friend, Josiah the crow, waiting on the ledge to come in.

Josiah was larger than an average crow and so black and sleek that at times, in the right patch of sunlight, he reflected various glimmers of blue. Vladimir hurried over and opened the window. Josiah hopped over the threshold and fluttered across to the large, round oak desk in the center of the room, upsetting a cup filled with pens and causing a few papers to drift to the floor.

"Oh, do be careful, Josiah," remarked Vladimir as he bent down to pick up the mess.

"Never mind that," replied Josiah. "You told the windy trees to send for me and here I am." And then, looking over at Army passed out on the couch, he asked forebodingly, "Is that him?"

Vladimir set the papers back down on the desk and righted the cup of pens. The two old friends stared at Army passed out on the sofa. A strange quiet filled the room as they both prepared to step into a deep and dangerous future.

"I do believe it is. All signs pointed to his coming and well, you can see for yourself, he's here," Vladimir said.

"I always thought he'd be bigger," Josiah said, as he leaped up from the table and glided over to where Army lay, causing the papers Vladimir had just picked up off the floor to scatter once more.

"Josiah!" Vladimir cried in exasperation. "Please be careful!"

But the crow wasn't listening as he landed on the couch's arm next to Army's feet and continued to stare at the boy. Could this really be him? The Arrival that Vladimir the High Patternologist had predicted so long ago? The hope fulfilled? The promise kept?

Perhaps now is a good time to explain exactly what a Patternologist does. Simply put, a Patternologist's job is to observe and record the events occurring around them, to discern the connections between those events, and to predict the future based on the patterns. Patternologists must go through rigorous training on such subjects as coincidence, round time, and dimensionology before they get their divining scrolls. For instance, have you ever thought of a friend and then moments later they call you or you see them on the street? That is one type of coincidence that Patternologists would catalog, but they'd categorize it differently from a similar one where you *think* you see your friend on the street but it's not them and then, moments later, you actually run into the friend that you had mistakenly thought the other person was! A bit confusing, but this is the kind of thing Patternologists deal with all of the time, not to mention the myriad other patterns such as weather, accidents, and mysterious sounds. Since being ordained, Vladimir focused his life's work on the patterns dealing with The Arrival.

"Is he dead?" Josiah enquired.

"Of course not, you silly goose," explained Vladimir as he walked over to stand behind the bird, careful not to tread upon Army's outstretched hand. "He's just, uh, resting."

And if you can call having fainted 'resting', then that was what Army was doing up until that moment. Now, slowly returning to consciousness, Army kept his eyes closed and used the distraction of the animals' bickering to put his hand slowly back in his pocket, grip his Langdim Finder and begin to press the buttons in his nervous one-two pattern to try to calm his racing thoughts.

"I am not a silly goose!" cawed Josiah.

The lights in Vladimir's sanctum began to turn off and on, slowly increasing in frequency.

"Looks like your crystals need changing, Vladimir," Josiah said, looking about the room.

"I don't think…" began Vladimir, who trailed off as he saw that Army had begun flickering along with the lights.

"What's going on?" cried Josiah in astonishment. "I don't think this is the crystals at all!"

"No! It's not!" exhorted Vladimir. "Grab him before he disappears again!"

But they were too late. The boy continued to pop in and out of the animal's reality with increasing rapidity as the lights flashed off and on quicker and quicker, and then the strobing ceased, the lights went back to their steady glow and Army had vanished. One moment he was lying there on the couch and the next he was simply gone, leaving nothing but the wonder of his absence and the indentations on the furniture where he had lain.

"Just like last time," sighed Vladimir.

"Last time?" Josiah said.

CHAPTER 11

When Army opened his eyes again he didn't know what surprised him more, that he was lying flat on the floor looking up at Mr Finch and Mrs Czernowski's worried faces or that he wasn't looking at a pig.

"Och, dzięki Bogu!" cried Mrs Czernowski in Polish, and then continuing in English she said, "He's waking up!"

"Army can you hear me?" Mr Finch said with great anxiety.

Army felt a sense of calm excitement come over him. Years of experience bending school rules to the near breaking point had given him lightning reflexes when it came to getting out of trouble. His current horizontal position could be used to his advantage. Surreptitiously, Army turned his phone on to recording mode. It was a skill he developed during his many spying adventures around his neighborhood. A good secret agent is always prepared!

Then, after first pressing a button on his Finder with his other hand for luck, he moaned.

"Och, dzięki Bogu!" howled Mrs Czernowski again in Polish but this time Army heard it in plain English, "Oh, my god!"

It was working! Army moaned louder.

Mrs Czernowski turned to Mr Finch and said, "He's hurt! We're in trouble now!"

"In Polish," the principal whispered harshly. "He can hear us. He's coming to!"

Mrs Czernowski and Mr Finch then carried on their furtive conversation in Polish which now Army understood perfectly.

"Co zrobimy? (What will we do?)" Mrs Czernowski cried.

"Jest ok. Wyzdrowieje. Powiemy tylko, że potknął się i upadł, kiedy wykonywał szalony taniec, o którym mi opowiadałeś. (It's OK. He's going to be fine. We'll just say he tripped and fell when he was doing the crazy dance you told me about.)" Mr Finch explained.

"So," thought Army, "one of Mr Finch's languages is Polish!"

Now this was an interesting development!

"Game, set, and match, I do believe!" Army concluded to himself.

"But I was outside of the room on the phone when he fell over. It's my fault!" wailed Mrs Czernowski.

"No one knows that but you and I," replied Mr Finch conspiratorially.

"And me," Army chimed in, opening his eyes and giving them both a big 'I got you' smile.

"What?" the two grown-ups gasped in unison while looking down at Army.

"It's 'you and me' not 'you and I," Army said. "'No one knows but you and me' would be the grammatically correct way of saying it."

The adults just couldn't believe their ears.

"But you'd still be wrong because I know as well," Army continued. "I know you left a poor child unsupervised and that he might have a possible concussion as a result!"

"You… you understood us? You speak Polish?" Mrs Czernowski asked, astonished.

"Sure. My grandfather on my mom's side of the family taught it to me," Army lied.

"Please, Abraham, I was just out of the room for a second calling my sister," Mrs Czernowski lied back to him.

"I didn't know Mr Finch was your sister," Army said, relishing this turn of events.

"You… you were listening!" his detention teacher exclaimed.

"All right, all right," Mr Finch interjected, "no harm no foul."

With that, Army started moaning again and rubbing his head.

"Oh, get up, you're fine," Mr Finch said, and then to cover all the bases he continued, "Listen Abraham, let's just forget the whole thing and you can go run along and enjoy the rest of recess, OK?"

Army saw his opening and pounced, "Sure thing, Mr Finch, just OK my passing French class and I'll be on my way."

"Nice try, Abraham," Mr Finch countered, "but the word of a delinquent student against a teacher and a principal is not going to carry any weight."

Army took out his phone and turning it towards his antagonists he pressed the send button on his recording app and proudly said, "I just e-mailed a recording of the last five minutes to myself, Mr Finch. How's that for initiative?"

Mr Finch knew that if this incident got reported he might lose his job. He was also aware that Mr Dumont wanted to be rid of Army anyway and so he acquiesced and said, "OK, no French classes, but you still have to submit the final project for a passing grade. Deal, Abraham?" And he held his hand out to help Army up.

"Just one more thing," Army beamed. "No more Abraham. From now on you both call me Army like everyone else does."

"Okay, Army," the principal replied, pronouncing Army's name through pursed lips as though he had just sucked on a lemon. "Now get up and we'll never mention today's unfortunate accident again."

"Then it's a deal," Army said. He stood up, checked to make sure his Langdim Finder was secure in his pocket, and ran out the door.

"Another victory for Army!" he smiled to himself and he headed outside to play.

CHAPTER 12

Vladimir looked up from his table trough and regarded his dear friend Josiah.

"It was him and he'll be back," he said.

"Of course he will be, Vladimir," returned Josiah.

"Don't mock me you old crow."

"I'm not a mocking bird," explained Josiah, and then added tauntingly, "You predicted The Arrival; it's just that you never said it'd be so quickly followed by 'The Departure!'"

"Ha, ha," Vladimir replied in despondent monotone.

Josiah pecked vaguely at the seeds on his plate. Vladimir slurped up a few sips of his gruel. The ancient grandfather clock by the fireplace ticked. Outside, the sun was setting and the wind had picked up again. The first star of the night glinted like a chip of ice on a cold blue sea.

"So, what happens now?" Josiah asked.

"What always happens. We wait. We work. We go on. And then we wait some more." Vladimir answered.

"But the patterns," Josiah said, approaching a now very sensitive subject, "maybe, and I'm saying this with all due respect Vladimir, but maybe you missed something."

Vladimir snorted and rose from the dining table. It very rarely happened, but he had lost his appetite. He waddled over to the fireplace and began to place the kindling wood around the waiting logs[6]. Just then the bell rang, signaling that someone was at the door downstairs at the ground level wanting to come in.

"That will be Lucy," Vladimir said over his shoulder to Josiah. He made no move to let her in. Instead, he continued stocking the hearth.

Josiah didn't know which he hated more. That Vladimir was always right, or that the pig knew that the curious crow wouldn't be able to help himself and would fly down to see if it really was her.

It was. Lucy the sheep was waiting patiently on the tower's doorstep enjoying the cool fingers of the evening breeze on her woolen back as Josiah alighted on the lever that opened the heavy wooden door. As always, Josiah marveled at how quietly and efficiently his weight engaged the various gears and counterweights to interact and swing open the entryway. He had once asked Vladimir just exactly who had built the tower, its machines, orbs, and instruments. Vladimir's answer was to look off far away as if into an unseen dimension and just whisper, "It was a long time ago."

---

[6] A note to my readers: The smart animals have figured out how to do things like make fires, brew tea, and to use tools and things that most humans use. They've evolved unique methods to overcome their lack of opposable thumbs by being quite clever and thus have arrived at their own means for such accomplishments. For instance, at this point in our tale Vladimir used a combination of snout and hoof (not to be confused with the old pub in town called *Ye Olde Snout and Hoof Inn*) to place the kindling, and a rather ingenious use of flint on the floor to create the ignition. However, to keep the flow of our tale from being interrupted every time an animal does an action one normally associates solely with humans, I will put it to your imagination how each task is done. Teamwork is a grand thing indeed and we're in this thing together!

"Hello, Josiah," Lucy purred. Now everyone knows that sheep don't purr they bleat, but Lucy very rarely bleated and her soft, compassionate voice seemed more like a baritone trill. She was a lady of, as she put it, "The utmost comportment" and her speech was more like the satisfied thrumble of a large, contented cat than the complaining cry of a common sheep.

"Hello, Lucy, come on in. Vladimir's upstairs preparing a fire," Josiah said, greeting his friend.

"A fire? Did you two quarrel?" asked Lucy, for a fire was prepared for only two reasons amongst the higher animals. The first reason was quite specific and that was, obviously, for the warmth a good blaze provided. The second reason was more general in nature, that being for storytelling, singing, and more seriously, for the settling of disagreements.

"Not really," Josiah said, as he landed onto Lucy's shoulder and she began to make her way up the winding steps to the top room.

"Not really?" Lucy countered.

"I just inquired if, perhaps, he had missed something in the patterns."

"Oh, Josiah," Lucy reprimanded the bird, "Vladimir is quite touchy about things like that, you know."

"I know, I know, it's just…" Josiah stopped himself. He wasn't sure how much he should reveal. The enormity of the last hour's events seemed to caution discretion and yet Vladimir didn't say anything about keeping it confidential.

"It's just the lights," Lucy said, finishing Josiah's sentence for him.

"You know?" Josiah squawked.

"Of course I know. Everyone knows. Everyone saw. Why do you think I'm here? The others sent me." And with that they had finally reached the top of the stairs and entered Vladimir's Pattorabory: the working place of the land's most highly esteemed Patternologist. At that precise moment the aforementioned Patternologist was rolling in a giant tub of mud in front of a roaring, sparking fire, his day's wardrobe neatly folded over a mahogany clothes valet.

"Hello, Lucy!" Vladimir exclaimed, identifying his guest without needing to turn to see her.

"Knew it was her from the patterns, eh?" Josiah surrendered.

"I deduced it was her from the patterns when the bell rang but I *knew* it was her by the wonderful scent of lavender on wool as you came up the steps. Lucy always stops by the lavender fields for a tumble on her way to visit me, isn't that right my dear?"

"Right you are, Super-Nose," Lucy chided with a slight smile, for the pig and the sheep were old, dear friends who had the kind of relationship that thrived on insults and jokes on one another.

"Ha!" said Vladimir joining in the fun, "It's not as if you were worth a scent!"

Lucy stared back blankly as Josiah simply raised his eyes and sighed quietly. Neither of them were going to give Vladimir the gift of a moan at the creaky old pun.

"Scent! Get it? Cent like 'money' but spelled like when one is sniffing a smell!" Vladimir splashed about turning in his tub to stare them down. "Oh, you two are hopeless!"

Standing in the doorway, Lucy and Josiah kept their straight faces held for a few moments longer and then finally burst out laughing, not at the pun so much as at the vexed look on their muck-covered host. Vladimir's frustrated face broke into a grin as he motioned to the cushions in front of the fireplace.

"Come in, come in you two, and shut the door. Take a seat and I'll join you in a moment," Vladimir laughed, grateful to the fire for warming up not only the room but the mood as well. He quickly showered off the cleansing mud (using rainwater that ran down from the gutter encircling the dome, through a spout above the pig's head, and subsequently back out through a drain beneath his hooves) and then he wrapped himself in his big fluffy red bathrobe and plonked himself down in his straw bed by the fire. Picking up an apple from the bowl he kept nearby, he finally turned back to his guests.

"No and yes," he said to Lucy, answering her questions before they were asked.

"Yes, no… what?" said Josiah looking at Lucy.

Lucy, long used to Vladimir's irritating habit of always knowing what animals were going to say before they said it, peered steadily back into the giant pig's eyes and considered asking a random question just to throw him off. This occasion, however, was too important to get sidetracked from. So instead, she merely said, "So, you mean, he arrived but he's not here now."

"Exactly," Vladimir replied.

This quiet understanding of things between Lucy and Vladimir drove Josiah crazy. Why couldn't they just have a normal conversation without always having to prove they were one step ahead?

"Arrival and departure within minutes of each other," Josiah told Lucy, initiating a stern look from Vladimir. "Well, it's true, Vladimir, but I'm not blaming you."

"You predicted The Arrival, Vladimir, and it's happened. This is cause for celebration, not concern," Lucy said, looking on the bright side of things, as was her wont.

"No, Josiah's right. How could I have missed the briefness of it? I always thought he would lead us into a new age, the golden times," Vladimir moaned.

"He still might. Good things happen in threes my dear fellows, and he's only been here twice," Lucy rejoined.

"That we know of," Josiah added, and he was rewarded with dark looks from both of his friends this time around.

CHAPTER 13

The rest of Army's school day went by in a blur. It was all so fantastic; understanding foreign languages, traveling to alternate realities, blackmailing the principal, it was like something out of a book. Army spent the time before the final bell of the day playing the events over and over in his head. The looks on his teachers' faces when he spoke so fluently were priceless but how did he do it? He was no stranger to daydreaming in class, in fact if there was a class about daydreaming he'd pass with honors, but they never seemed so real before. The talking pig in the strange tower. It had seemed so tangible but now it was fading in his memory like a dream from years ago.

He walked about in a shimmering daze going to his afternoon classes, retrieving his book bag from his locker, and boarding the crowded school bus home. His body moved instinctively but his thoughts were far away as he sat down and looked out of the bus window at the sun falling low in the sky.

"I said, HELLO!"

Army broke out of his reverie to see Willie looking quizzically at him.

"Why are you shouting at me?" Army asked as the bus continued loading up with students.

"Because I said hello like five times and you didn't answer me. What's wrong with you?"

"Well," Army imagined answering, "I've been in the castle tower of a talking pig and I've tricked Mr Finch into passing me out of French class in advance."

But what he actually said was, "Nothing. I'm fine."

"Fine? Wendy just walked by to her seat in the back of the bus and smiled at you and you didn't even so much as nod at her. I thought she was like your true love or something."

Wendy smiled at him? Army whipped around in his seat to look back and see Wendy in a deep whispered conversation with her best friend Cathy. Blonde with dark green eyes and slightly taller than Wendy, Cathy always seemed to be guarding Wendy from Army, like a Golden Retriever guide dog protecting its owner from oncoming traffic. They both looked up at him and started giggling. Army turned right back around and looked out the window at the darkening, late afternoon sky.

Willie continued, "She must have heard about your visit to the principal's office."

"How would she know about that?" Army replied.

"Are you kidding me?" Willie said, as the bus pulled away from the curb. "Everyone is talking about it. How did you suddenly know all that French? I thought you hated French."

"I do, I mean, I did, oh, I don't know what I mean."

How *did* Army suddenly know French, Spanish, and Polish? What was that place he transported too? Was it a daydream? Army started getting anxious about it all, and Wendy and Cathy's laughter wasn't helping any. He put his hand in his pocket, took out The Langdim Finder and started absent-mindedly pressing the buttons.

"Don't look now Army but Cathy is heading our way," Willie said.

The button pushing increased in speed and pressure and suddenly the lights in the bus began flickering off and on.

"Off and on," thought Army, "Just like before."

He looked wildly about him. No one else seemed to notice.

"Here she comes, you better put your toy away or she may ask you about it," Willie cautioned.

Army looked down at the little blue device he was unconsciously playing with, shoved it back into his pocket, put his hands on his lap and peered out of the window again, trying to act as nonchalantly as possible.

The lights snapped back to normal. And finally, for Army, the penny dropped. The lights, the languages, the alternate dimensions, all of it happened while he was pressing the buttons and they stopped happening when he stopped pressing them.

"Willie!" he shouted out loud in awe. "I know what's causing the flashing lights!"

"What flashing lights?"

"Don't you see them?" Army replied, his voice rising in excitement.

"What are you talking about?

"The Langdim Finder!" Army exclaimed.

CHAPTER 14

The animals held their breath as the lights in Vladimir's chamber flickered momentarily and then resumed their steady glow. They looked at the shining orbs and then at each other and slowly, in unison, they exhaled. It was like feeling the tremor of an earthquake followed by focused silence and the uneasy sense that the big one was still to come.

"Does that mean he's here?" whispered Lucy.

Josiah flew to the window with Vladimir following behind him. They looked out into the night.

"It's too dark," Josiah complained, "I can't see a thing."

Vladimir opened the window, stuck his snout outside and took a big sniff.

"He's not there," he concluded.

"Vladimir, what's going on?" Josiah asked.

"Yes, Vladimir, what do the patterns say now?" Lucy joined in.

Vladimir walked over to his study table, sat down, picked up a scroll and opened it up. He mumbled a few words under his breath that sounded like calculations of some sort and then let out a long sigh.

"I don't understand. The tensions, coincidences and signs all pointed to The Arrival but there was nothing to indicate how brief it would be or that it might occur intermittently."

"Yes," said Lucy, "but what do the signs say now?"

"Now? Why the same things of course; the full moon, The Wishing Well, the floating girl. He should be here!"

Lucy pressed on, "But we already knew about those things and that's why you predicted The Arrival to begin with. But what has changed *since* he was here?"

"Since he was here?" Vladimir pondered this. "Since he was here! Of course! Thank you, Lucy!"

Vladimir sprung to his feet, grabbed the scroll and a pen from the cup and handed them to Josiah.

"Take notes, Josiah!" he shouted as he began to think out loud.

"The lights flickering, plus thoughts I was having about the infinite nature of the universe, plus the wind, multiplied by the smell of rosemary and musty, wet wool…"

"Musty, wet wool?" Lucy bridled.

"Not you, Lucy!" Josiah said. "Go on, Vladimir, go on!"

"Yes, yes, yes… well, that was it really and then there he was dancing in the field."

"How do you know he was dancing? Did you hear music?" Lucy asked.

"Music? No. You're right! There wasn't any music. I don't actually *know* he was dancing. That was an assumption on my part. Let's subtract that and substitute 'waving arms and hands about'."

"Maybe he was fighting something," Josiah suggested.

"No, his hands were open almost, now that I think of it, like he was protecting himself, as one would from a swarm of bees."

"Open-handed waving," Lucy said, chuckling a little bit, "got it."

"Open-handed. That's important somehow. Anything standing out from the background pattern is important," Vladimir said, quoting one of his own tenets.

"And then what happened?" Lucy asked.

"And then he vanished," Vladimir replied.

"But then he came back!" Josiah countered.

"Yes," Vladimir agreed, "about an hour later. I had gone out to the field to investigate. I was snuffling about collecting clues when the day seemingly turned to night and back to day again several times in quick succession and then, poof! There he was again!"

Vladimir had gotten a faraway look in his eyes as he remembered the miraculous manifestation.

"Dancing without music in the field?" Lucy asked.

"Hunh?" Vladimir shook his head. "No, he was standing, sort of stooped over with his hand to his ear as if he was listening to something. And then he spoke."

"He spoke?" Josiah said with surprise. "You never told me that part."

"Where was his other hand?" Lucy asked.

"His other hand? Why I never thought of that. It was in his pocket."

"His pocket?" Lucy chided. "Exactness of symbols is vital. You always tell us that."

"Yes, of course. He was wearing a brown jacket and his hand was in his pocket, as if he was holding onto something in there."

"Who cares?" Josiah shouted excitedly. "What did he say?"

"*Oh my god,*" Vladimir said.

"What's wrong?" Lucy asked.

"Nothing's wrong," Vladimir explained. "That's just what he said, *Oh my god.*"

"His god?" Josiah wondered. "Maybe he said, 'Hello, I'm God.' and you just heard him wrong. He was *introducing* himself to you."

"No, I don't think so because the next thing he did was call me a 'talking' pig as if that was something strange and then he passed out."

"Gods don't pass out," Josiah concluded.

"Well, this one did."

"What happened next, Vladimir, and don't leave anything out," Lucy intoned.

And so Vladimir recounted the rest of the circumstances of what they were now calling The Second Arrival while Josiah wrote down the Patternologist's calculations taking note of the boy waking up and passing out again, the lights, the departure, all of it. When he finished, Vladimir asked for the scroll and began to once again check and double-check what had been written down. It was at this point that Lucy made a most astute observation.

"After he passed out and was lying on your couch, you said his arm hung loosely and his hand was on the ground and you had to take care not to step on it."

"Yes, that's right," said Vladimir, feeling an instinctive tingle of excitement as on some level he knew where Lucy was headed with this line of thought.

"But moments later when the lights began changing and he began to disappear, you lunged to hold onto him but you didn't step on his hand."

"She's right," Josiah agreed. "He had put his hand back in his pocket."

"He was awake!" cried Vladimir. "Add that... no, wait, multiply that and divide by the amount of times his hand was in his pocket and... hold on, I've got it..."

But he was interrupted by Josiah, "He has something in his pocket that enables him to appear and disappear into our world!"

Ordinarily, being upstaged by the crow would have sent the pig into another one of his snits, but the revelation was too astounding for such petty emotions.

"The Langdim Finder!" all three friends shouted at once in joy and wonder.

CHAPTER 15

C athy giggled at Army's outburst. He looked up at her standing just behind him and gave her a sheepish smile.

"What did you say? What's a language finder?" Cathy asked.

Army just continued beaming at her, unsure of what to say or what to do. The school bus was the scene of his huge humiliation last week with Wendy and he had no desire to compete with it now.

"It's not a language finder," Willie spoke up seemingly in Army's defense. "It's his Langdim Finder. It takes him away to other worlds!"

"Thanks for the assist, Willie," Army thought sarcastically as he maintained his frozen grin.

"Oh really?" Cathy said with delight. "Can I see it, Army?"

"What? No. I mean, I don't have it with me," Army lied trying to regain his composure.

"But it's…" Willie started saying only to finish his sentence with a harsh gasp as Army dug his elbow into his friend's ribs.

"It's just a game we play to kill time on the bus!" Army interjected with a forced laugh.

The bus pulled over to the side of the road to make its first stop and three children got off to make their ways home. The bus driver shut the doors and headed back along his winding route.

"Well, Army, the reason I came over," Cathy started, and then, after a quick look towards the back of the bus at Wendy, continued, "was to see if you'll be trying out for the school musical this year."

That was a big deal in Army's school. The two guys who could count on being popular were the football captain and the male lead in the school musical. There was fierce competition for the part and his nemesis, old Mrs Czernowski, was the director. Of course, she loved to play the kids off of each other, gleefully enjoying sadistic thrills as the fledgling actors and actresses knocked themselves out trying to get noticed by her. It was nuts and Army was not going to put up with it. He actually had a good chance at the lead because, let's face it, Army was nothing if not dramatic! Emboldened by the just-discovered powers of his plastic talisman and his annoyance at Cathy and Wendy's whispering about him, Army figured it was time for a little revolutionary spirit. The girls were hatching a plot and he'd have none of it.

"School musical?" Army said. "You mean Czernowski's psychic torture?"

"Psychic torture? No, the musical, the school musical," Cathy replied, confused by what Army had said. How come he always made everything so complicated?

"Yeah, right. Every year she holds auditions and all the kids kowtow to her every whim vying to get a part. But the best roles always go to her biggest sycophants, so why bother? I could write a better musical myself. Everyone should just boycott Czernowski's annual circus of pain!"

The school bus began signaling for another stop. Cathy was getting upset.

"It's just a silly old musical, Army," she said, "it's supposed to be fun."

"It's *supposed* to be," Army replied, getting more on fire as he started feeling trapped by Cathy and anxious that she kept looking back at Wendy, "but it's not. It's just all the kids running around like worker ants for the horrid lizard-queen chorus teacher!"

Cathy couldn't take it anymore. Couldn't Army see she was asking this for Wendy's benefit? She shot back, "Well, you should know something about that, shouldn't you? Handing Wendy a scroll of servants, for heaven's sake!"

At that Army exploded, but unfortunately it was at the precise moment when the school bus had come to a complete stop and opened its doors for children to exit. You know that moment when the sounds of the engine and the road noise cease and everyone lowers their voices or stops talking until the bus starts up again? It was at that moment that Army yelled, "Well, can I help it if I like Wendy and was just trying to make her happy?"

"Oh. My. God." Army said to himself, as he turned bright red and broke into a sweat. Everyone on the bus was looking at him.

"Embarrassing," Willie whispered in a sing-song voice.

And then all of the children started laughing and screaming with delight at Army's outburst. Army looked down the aisle and saw Wendy looking at him with –what was that look? Pity? Horror? He jumped to his feet, pulled his hood up, ran to the front of the bus and down the steps, leaping off the last one and speeding down the street as fast as his legs could take him as the students' laughter faded into the distance behind him, but still echoed as loud as ever in his head.

CHAPTER 16

The school bus pulled back from the bus stop and continued on its way. It passed by Army who had slowed down to a sullen walk, unintentionally giving his classmates one more opportunity to taunt him by yelling out the windows at the boy who would be king.

"Hey Army, the pharaoh called and asked which pyramid is Wendy's!"

"Make me happy too, Army!"

"Army loves Wendy!"

Army pulled his hood tighter around his head and trudged on.

"That's it," Army grumbled to himself, "not only aren't I trying out for the stupid musical, but I'm never going back to school again!"

The October air grew chilly as the sun started to touch down on the horizon far beyond the town. Army had gotten off of the bus a few stops earlier than normal in order to escape further public humiliation, and he was now walking by a series of shops that included the local pizzeria. He could smell the sweet tomato and onion sirens calling him out of the falling night and into the steamy warm pizza shop.

"Army! Ciao, come stai, eh?" Lorenzo, the shop's owner and main pizza maker, greeted Army. He always spoke a few phrases in Italian to Army when he'd come in and he had taught Army the proper responses.

"Sto bene. E tu, come stai?" Army replied, saying he was fine, though he didn't really mean it.

"Army, you don't look so happy. Rough day?" Lorenzo asked, genuinely concerned. He liked Army. The boy had a great imagination and Lorenzo always enjoyed hearing about his ideas and adventures.

"You wouldn't believe the half of it," Army sighed.

"Try me," Lorenzo urged.

"Let's just say that everything that could go wrong to a kid in school, did."

"Aw, now what could be so tragic?"

And it all came blurting out like somebody had shaken Army up and popped his cork, "Well, I'm having these weird blackouts or time jumps or something where I end up in this alternate dimension with a talking pig and it got me in trouble with the principal but it doesn't matter because I understand Polish for some reason all of a sudden and Cathy wants me to be in the school musical but Czernowski's in charge of that and she's awful so I don't want to do it but maybe Wendy will be in it and then I would want to do it and…"

Lorenzo, who didn't understand a word of Army's rapid-fire meltdown, put his hands in the air like he was surrendering and said, "Whoa, whoa, Army. I'm not sure what this is all about, but it sounds like you need a fresh slice of Lorenzo's magic "cheer-you-up" pizza!"

"Sure, Lorenzo," Army mumbled, certain that no one in the world understood him.

"Not 'Sure Lorenzo'. Sì per favore, Lorenzo!" the pizza maker chided as he put a slice in the oven to warm up.

"Sì per favore, Lorenzo," Army said, still in his sad tone.

Lorenzo sighed. Bad moods can be contagious and now he too was feeling down, having failed to brighten up Army's day. "I hope the pizza helps," Lorenzo said to himself as he went to the sink to wash a few dishes while Army's slice was heating up.

Army went and sat in a booth to wait for his slice. He slumped down and shoved his hands in his pockets. The Langdim Finder! In his rush to get away from the embarrassment on the bus he had forgotten all about it. He took it out and held it in his hands. He looked up and saw Lorenzo looking back at him with a concerned expression while drying a plate. Army felt bad now about upsetting Lorenzo's usual happy mood and that's when he finally had the idea to try out the powers of The Langdim Finder on purpose. Army started pushing the buttons, feeling equally nervous that it was going to work or that it wasn't. He began wishing he spoke Italian. He pictured Italy on the map and the leaning tower of Pisa; which Army always called 'The Leaning Tower of Pizza,' and imagined that it was just a giant stack of tottering pizza boxes.

Lorenzo turned back to the oven, opened it up, and brought out Army's hot slice. Army got up from the booth and approached the counter while furiously pressing The Finder's buttons and trying to remember some of the phrases the pizza chef had taught him.

"Your slice is ready, Army. I hope it you like it," Lorenzo said with worried eyes.

Here was Army's chance to make up for bringing his troubles into the pizzeria.

"Grazie!" he said, using the first word Lorenzo had taught him.

Lorenzo brightened up to hear Army use Italian and so he gave his usual reply, "Prego!"

He then turned to start working on a new order but stopped in his tracks when he heard Army continue, "E posso dire che a fai la migliore pizza in della città!" (And may I say you make the best pizza in town).

"Che cosa? (What?)" Lorenzo asked with astonishment.

"Amo la tua pizza, Lorenzo! (I love your pizza, Lorenzo!)" Army exclaimed.

"You love my pizza?" Lorenzo continued. "I know you do, but how do you know to say this in Italian? It is fantastico!"

Happy that he had cheered Lorenzo back up but feeling like he should keep his new power secret, Army just said, "Mi sono allenato su internet, Lorenzo. (I've been practicing on the internet, Lorenzo.)"

"Dio mio! This boy he is amazing! My favorite boy! Here, here, this slice is on Lorenzo!"

And with that he handed Army his slice.

"Grazie, Lorenzo, lo mangerò tornando a casa. (Thank you, Lorenzo, I'm going to eat it on my way home.)" Army said with gusto, as he headed out the door and then, over his shoulder, he added, "Arrivederci! (Goodbye!)"

"Arrivederci, Army," laughed Lorenzo. "Arrivederci!"

CHAPTER 17

Vladimir was at his research table holding the scroll up at arm's length and poring over his calculations. Josiah was peering out the window into the darkness, and Lucy was preparing a stiff blend of black peppermint tea. It was going to be a long night.

The Langdim Finder was the stuff of legend. An object existing in all dimensions at the same time. The key to a thousand doors. The twilight line between the wild and enlightened animals.

"Stuff and nonsense!" exclaimed Vladimir as he threw down the scroll and began to pace back and forth along the dais that the patterning table stood upon.

Josiah and Lucy let Vladimir be. It was no use approaching him when he was in the middle of trying to discern a pattern that was frustrating him. He snorted and fumed while Lucy brought the tea tray over to the fireside table and announced its readiness. Josiah flew over to his perch by the hearth as Lucy curled up with her cup.

"Be a dear, Josiah," Lucy said softly, "and relight the fire."

"What's the occasion, Lucy?" Josiah asked.

"I believe a tale needs to be told," she answered.

Josiah hopped down to the hearth, grabbed the flint, and scraped it sharply along the stone apron to create the spark needed to reignite the fire. Soon, a blaze was once again filling the room with warmth and cozy wooden smells.

Winking at Josiah, Lucy called over to the pacing, porcine Patternologist, "Vladimir, come join us. The tea is ready and the fire is delightful."

"What?" Vladimir said, disturbed from his vexations. "Oh, no thanks. I can't stop now. I must figure out when the next arrival will be."

"And you won't figure it out pacing around and muttering to yourself," Lucy implored. "Come and sit with us. The tea will help to clear your head."

Knowing it would be quicker to just do what he was told than to argue with Lucy, Vladimir joined his friends by the fire.

Once Vladimir was settled in his straw with a cup at hoof, Lucy said to him, "Tell us the story, Vladimir."

"Which story, Lucy?"

"The story of The Langdim Finder, of course, and how our world, Langdimania, got its name."

"Oh, Lucy," Josiah wailed, "we've all heard that story hundreds of times!"

And indeed they had, for it was *the* bedtime story that all little animals heard while growing up.

"Hrumph," Vladimir griped along with the crow. "You went to the trouble of a fire-tea for no reason Lucy. It's a story we all know by heart and does not need a retelling now. I have more important things to think about."

"But Vladimir, Josiah, we've never heard the story while we were aware that The Langdim Finder had actually arrived!" Lucy revealed.

"Hmmm," Josiah hummed while thinking aloud, "she's right, Vladimir, but I don't see how that changes things."

But Vladimir did. It was a disruption of a pattern and so it had importance. He took a sip of tea, as did the others, and then he began, "It is the story of stories, isn't it? The brave hero, the floating girl, the mystery."

The fire crackled as a log shifted and sent sparks flying up the flue; a good sign that the flames welcomed the telling of the story. Peering over their steaming cups at each other, the animals had that delicious feeling of time stopping and taking a seat with them to listen along.

"Before the enlightenment," Vladimir recited, "before we had language, when our world had no name, a crow…"

"My great-great-great-a-whole-bunch-more-greats grandfather!" Josiah boasted.

"Don't interrupt, Josiah," admonished Lucy.

"Just saying, is all," a chagrined Josiah responded.

"Anyway, a crow," Vladimir looked over at Josiah, smiled, and continued, "and not just any crow but Josiah's honored ancestor, Joseph…"

At that, Josiah perked right back up. Crows do wear their hearts on their wings, after all.

Vladimir continued, "… found The Langdim Finder, or, as some would contend, it found him! As it is today so it was back then that the animals fell into two tribes separated by their environments: the animals of F'arm and the beasts of F'orest. An uneasy truce existed between them and all was fine, as long as they didn't stray across the isthmus that separated the two groups. Occasionally, a wolf or fox would invade to hunt for dinner, but we F'armians had long ago learned that posting the bulls by the border discouraged that sort of thing quite effectively."

Vladimir took another sip of tea, relishing its sharp clean bite, and then continued on with the tale.

"One day, Joseph was flying above the F'orest River when he was almost blinded by a glint of light reflected off of something lying in the sand along the banks of the waterway. Intrigued, the big black bird spiraled down for a closer look, wary of any F'orestians that might be hungry for a crow lunch. The object was half buried and as the crow circled above it, he was dazzled by its glittering iridescence. Looking all around for any signs of predators and being satisfied that he was in the clear, Joseph dove down and grabbed the bauble. He then ascended, climbing higher and higher until he was well above the trees and on his way, far from the peering eyes of F'orest.

"The sun had risen to the center of the sky and felt good upon his back. He approached his tree, where the local murder[7] of crows was basking in the warm sunshine and descended, holding his prize in his mouth so as to leave his claws free to gain a claw hold of his branch. He heard several of his friends caw and looking up he saw that he and his new acquisition were the center of *Corvus* attention."

At this point, Vladimir took a look at Josiah and said, "Please excuse me if I misstate anything about your dear ancestor."

"It's all right, Vladimir, we all know the story," Josiah consoled.

"Please go on, Vladimir," Lucy rejoined.

---

[7] Everyone knows that the collective noun for cows is a herd, but did you know that for crows it can be a 'flock' or a 'murder'? For owls it's a 'parliament' and for tigers an 'ambush'. Cool, right? Perhaps you can discover more on your own, but for now let's get back to Vladimir's story.

"Well, amidst the ruckus, Joseph tightly clutched his treasure, wondering if he should fight or take flight as those were the only two choices his primitive..." and then quickly editing himself for Josiah's sake Vladimir continued, "Er, I mean, the only two choices his *uncomplicated* brain could think of. If only he could interpret his friends' intentions as they called back and forth to each other excitedly. And then suddenly, The First Manifestation occurred!"

"Hallelujah!" Lucy cried out, and the other two animals looked at her with surprise, as she very rarely erupted in such a manner.

"I mean," said Lucy, quickly regaining her composure, "who would like another spot of tea?"

Vladimir and Josiah laughed out loud, and, if sheep could blush, that is exactly what Lucy would have done at that moment. Instead, she quickly rose to put another kettle up to boil.

"A good time for a short break," Vladimir said, as he made a move to take care of those things that one needs to take care of during short breaks from long tales.

CHAPTER 18

With his spirits buoyed by his successful use of The Langdim Finder, Army walked happily through town toward home. The cool night air only served to enhance the delicious warm taste of his take-away pizza, and everything around him seemed a bit fresher and more exciting. He enjoyed looking at the Halloween displays in the shop windows. The masks of goblins and superheroes, the witches' brooms and the devils' pitchforks, the grinning Jack O' Lanterns, and the startled black cat cutouts with their backs arched and their fur on end. All of the shops participated in the annual event. Mr Wu's China Palace had even placed haystacks topped with traditional baskets of fruit on the steps leading up to its entrance.

Standing in front of Mr Wu's, Army finished his slice and wiped his greasy hands on the napkin that Lorenzo had provided him. He bunched the napkin up and, not seeing a trash basket nearby, he shoved the paper ball into his jacket pocket and took out his Langdim Finder, eager to give it another try.

Army started pressing the buttons while trying to think of any Chinese words he might know until he realized he actually didn't know any. Frustrated, he started to walk on and then stopped when he saw the sidewalk display that held the menu for the restaurant. Army saw that each dish was listed in both Mandarin and English.

"I wonder if it'll work if I stare at the Chinese characters while thinking of the dish they represent," Army thought. And a brilliant idea it was too, for as he did so, he witnessed the characters turn into their English equivalents right before his eyes!

"Wa, hěn hǎo yòng! (Wow, it's working!)" Army cried, and he ran up the steps into Wu's.

The restaurant was quiet, with only one table of early diners being served. A pretty hostess wearing a blue satin dress with the image of a silver dragon woven down its side welcomed Army and asked, "Hello, are you meeting someone here?"

"Bù, wǒ zhǐshì xiǎng shì shì shuō yīxià hànyǔ, (No, I just wanted to try speaking in Chinese)" Army said, delighting the girl.

"Hǎo shénqí! Nǐ de hànyǔ hěn bùcuò.. (You surprised me! You speak Chinese very well!)" she replied excitedly. "Nǐ zài nǎ'er xué de hànyǔ? (Where did you learn to speak Chinese?)"

Army thought quickly and replied, "Wǒ yǒu yīgè ei-pee-pee (I have an app for it!)!"

The girl laughed and told Army that he was a very smart young man. She beamed a beautiful smile at him and gave him a free fortune cookie. Army thanked her, in Chinese of course, and headed back into the evening. Realizing with a start that he was now late getting home, he raced down the sidewalk dodging in and out of the other pedestrians with his Langdim Finder held high in front of him while he shouted in Mandarin before it could fade away, "Gěi Army rànglù, shénqí shàonián láile!! (Make way for Army the wonder boy!)"

CHAPTER 19

The animals settled back down in front of the refreshed fire with newly brewed teas and high spirits.

Vladimir continued the tale, "In the middle of a panic over the intentions of his comrades, Joseph had a transcendent revelation. He could understand his flock; they had gained language!

'Why is he hiding it?' Joseph heard one bird say.

'Friend, come show us,' he heard another crow caw.

'We're your brothers and sisters, don't be scared,' a third bird called.

"It took a few seconds of wonderment before Joseph realized these weren't his own thoughts but the speech of the crows, and that the raucous chattering of the birds weren't cries of attack or retreat but rather had grander intentions behind them.

'Look at him!'

'Is he going to share it?'

'He's a lucky bird!'

"And then it happened, for the first time ever in our history, an animal gave a speech!

'My friends,' Joseph began, using a newly evolved form of traditional Caw that, miraculously, his flock was now able to understand, 'please forgive me. When I returned to our tree with the shining stone, I selfishly planned to keep it in my nest. It fascinated me and so I didn't see you as my brothers and sisters but as enemies, owls scheming to part me from my prize. Mere moments ago I didn't have thoughts that turned into sentences of reason; I simply felt a red mist of fear.'

"Joseph's audience was enraptured, each and every crow confident that they were present at one of those turning moments when everything changes forever. Joseph continued, 'But the fog of avarice lifted as I became aware that you weren't cawing for my destruction but were merely being curious, as is our nature. It's as if I was blind but could now see, deaf but could now hear. Today is the birth of a new crow and this magic stone is our birthday gift. Yes, our gift, not mine. True, it was I who found the stone, but its magic has resonated through our entire clan. Let our throats sing songs of joy and spread the message to all the animals of F'arm that this is a new world described and brought forth with words!'

"The murder of crows cheered and beat their wings, rejoicing in the ecstatic moment of newfound clarity.

'Tell us, where did you find the shiny stone?' cried out a young crow.

'In the sand near F'orest River,' Joseph replied, and instantly the water that ran through the land of the beasts now had a name, as did the land itself. Joseph looked around excitedly and proclaimed, 'And we live in the land of F'arm.'

'How do I suddenly know the name of the land we live in?' thought Joseph to himself. 'And how am I hearing what I'm thinking in my head?' he thought some more; and thus the first philosopher of F'arm was born."

A log in the fire suddenly split in two with a crackling sound and once again a shimmer of sparks flew up the flue.

"As if it knew what was coming," observed Josiah.

CHAPTER 20

A fter Army had left the room, Mr Finch said to Mrs Czernowski, "We can't let him get away with this."

"There's nothing we can do," Mrs Czernowski replied disconsolately.

"There's always something one can do if you show initiative!" Mr Finch said, proudly quoting himself while Mrs Czernowski turned her head so that the principal couldn't see her roll her eyes, just as every student did when he said things like that. "We just need to get something worse on young Mr Allen than he has on us."

"Like what?"

"This is Abraham Armstrong Allen we're talking about; he does something at least slightly criminal every day of his life!"

"Yes, but he's *proud* of it, it's not something we can threaten him with."

It's true, one cannot be blackmailed if one has no shame. Army could be embarrassed, especially where Wendy was concerned, but he couldn't be threatened with exposure over his various antics since he already glorified in them!

"And besides," Mrs Czernowski continued, "You can't blackmail a blackmailer because they can just blackmail you back. It's a stand-off."

"You're right," Mr Finch concurred, "but there has to be a solution."

Mrs Czernowski thought about this. Getting kids to do what she wanted was her specialty. The power of casting the musical, her abusive body odor, her piercing stare over her glasses, were all delicious weapons in her armory, and she reveled in their use. Now that this arsenal was denied to her, the loss was grievous and had depressed her considerably but the principal's drive for a plan had inspired her and suddenly she had an idea.

"If we can't threaten him by exposing some nefarious prank he's pulled, perhaps we can threaten to take away something he cherishes," she burbled.

"Something he cherishes? Yes, yes, that might work, but what?" Mr Finch wondered.

CHAPTER 21

Despite his protestations to the contrary, the next day saw Army in school as usual and, unlike the day before, he tried his best to keep a low profile. On the school bus he sat in the front seat on the same side that the door opened. This way kids would already have boarded the bus and headed towards the back before seeing him, and that included Cathy and Wendy. Army stared out of the window and, though he had The Langdim Finder with him, he kept his hand off of it to avoid any more incidents.

Once in school, Army timed his arrival to each class to be just seconds before the bell so that no one would have a chance to talk to him. During lunch and recess, Army went to the school library instead of outside to play. The place was empty of classmates. It was calming. Through the Palladian windows, Army could see the afternoon sun had passed its apex and had begun its descent, filtering rays of gold, filled with dancing patterns of dust, throughout the room.

Army wandered the aisles of books, feeling a bit sleepy as one quite often does after lunch. The bindings of the various novels and research books began to blend into one another as he walked past them aisle by aisle.

"Did you ever notice that aisle and isle sound the same?" said a voice just behind Army.

Army swiveled around but no one was there. Had he fallen into a sleepy daydream? He turned back around and didn't recognize which section of the library he was in. He looked up at the books to orientate himself but they all had the same title, *At Last* - or so it seemed that they did until he rubbed his eyes and looked again and he now saw that the books all had their unique names back, and the one he had focused on had changed its title to *Atlas*.

Army felt impelled to take a look, and so he took down the oversized book, carried it to one of the highly polished reading tables, and laid it down. It had a beautiful dark green cover with an intricate design of several globe-like spheres made of embossed golden thread. Army opened the book to leaf through pages of old maps of the world. Or at least at first glance they seemed to be so. But these must have been of very old countries in areas he had never heard of before. Some of the continents looked like the ones he knew, but as if someone was drawing their reflections in a strangely curved mirror. Feeling slightly uneasy by the events surrounding him, Army allowed his hand to take hold of The Langdim Finder and to begin pushing one of the buttons slowly in and out. He continued turning the pages with his other hand, fascinated by the landmasses that were swirling into impossible shapes, like clouds in the sky that played tricks on his eyes. Army felt dizzy yet cozily warm as the lights in the room began to flicker and his head drooped forward like when one begins to fall asleep in front of the TV. For a few seconds he nodded off, until the end of recess bell rang and woke him with a start. The lights were steady now as Army looked around and saw the librarian calmly marking books at her desk. He leaned back on the hind legs of his chair and balanced there, trying to recall the image he saw in the brief sleep he had under the fluttering lights. But he could only recall a vague image of the pig and crow from his previous, what he was now calling 'weird dreams', sitting in front of a fireplace, sipping tea with a sheep. His reverie was interrupted by the librarian, who reminded him that it was time to get back to class and that research books had to remain in the library.

Army got up from his table and reluctantly placed the book onto the returns cart. As he did so, an envelope fell out of it and onto the floor. Without hesitation, almost as if he had practiced for this moment, Army grabbed it and tucked it away in his back pocket before the librarian could see him, and then he walked straight out the door to his afternoon classes.

CHAPTER 22

Emboldened by the added drama that the flash from the fire provided, Vladimir continued with the story.

"As Joseph looked about, the correct name for each thing he saw immediately occurred to him. The glorious blue above became the 'sky', the white brush of mist became 'clouds', the firm piece of wood he was standing on became a 'branch'. Gazing at his flock, it seemed as if each bird that stood before him sparkled like a jewel in a crown. Looking at the one that asked him where he'd found the magic stone, Joseph said, 'You're Daniel,' and Daniel shouted out his new name in awe.

'But what's your name?' the newly dubbed Daniel asked.

"And just like that, his name came straight into his mind and he replied, 'Why, I'm Joseph, of course.'

'Me next!' shouted one of the crows.

'No, me! Me!' they all began to caw, and Joseph saw that he had a solemn duty to carry out. He bade his flock to form a line before him and, as each bird approached, Joseph gave them names: Lily, Aaron, Sam, and so on, until all were named and chattering excitedly in the new language they were discovering together.

'And now my friends,' Joseph cried out, 'let's name all that is F'arm!'

"And all at once the entire murder of crows took off from their various perches, a giant, undulating black cloud swarming across F'arm, blotting out the sky. Their huge shadow fell upon the land and the other animals looked up in surprise and terror. The sheep bayed, the pigs squealed, the cows mooed, and the horses whinnied. Squirrels and mice scurried to their hideaways, and dogs and cats lay flat and shivering on the ground.

"Seeing the fear and confusion the sudden arrival of the entire crow clan had caused, Joseph folded in his wings and dove to ground level, imploring the animals not to be alarmed, but they didn't understand; they only heard Joseph's cries for calm as the caws of a suddenly crazed bird. The commotion had reached the bulls who assumed that beasts were spotted, and they started a stampede toward F'orest.

'Oh no, this isn't good,' thought Joseph as he sped for the border, 'not good at all.'

'Follow me!' he yelled to his compatriots, and follow him they did, like a dark arrow over one hundred meters long shooting across the sky. They overtook the bulls, outdistanced them, and then, by Joseph's instruction, formed a flying wall to try to stop the herd. Closer and closer came the bulls. 'Stand fast!' Joseph cried out. 'Be brave! On my signal, let's all sing out our loudest, most beautiful note!'

"The bulls were now a mere fifty meters away, charging with their heads down and horns pointed forward, when Joseph finally gave the signal, 'Now!'

"The entire collection of birds sang as one; a glorious, wonderful cacophony that sounded like a clap of thunder startling the bulls and bringing them to a standstill. Dirt and dust filled the air as they slowly turned and ambled back to their field, and the crows took off back to their tree.

'Such a disaster!' Joseph castigated himself as he led his flock back home. 'If the bulls hadn't stopped, so many crows could've been injured, or worse!'

"It was all his fault and he had to make it right. And so, Joseph directed his flock to go ahead without him and he circled back to fly over F'arm on his own. When he arrived, he saw the animals drinking from the river, thirsty after their big scare.

'Perfect,' Joseph thought to himself. 'I can talk to all of them at once and give them the glorious news and their new names.'

"Gripping his sparkly stone, Joseph circled above the animals and proclaimed, 'Listen to me, creatures of F'arm. I am Joseph, king of the crows, and I bring you language!'

"Joseph looked down at the animals looking back up at him. He was glowing with importance. 'How they must be admiring me,' he thought grandly.

"And then, as if on cue, every animal started yelling at Joseph in his or her own fashion: baying, neighing, mooing, and squealing. The sound was deafening! Joseph grew angry and flew higher and shouted louder, 'Don't you see I'm only trying to help you?'

"But Joseph didn't realize that they couldn't understand him as they didn't yet have a language for his caws to be translated into.

"Higher and higher Joseph flew, shouting and cursing at the other animals until, in his rage, he shook The Langdim

Finder at them and cried, 'You don't deserve this gift!' Then, to his horror, the stone slipped from his claws and hurtled down, down, down into the river, disappearing from even his keen sight.

'Oh no!' Joseph cried out, circling above the river. 'I must find it! How could I have been so careless? All will be… will be…' Joseph's mind turned hazy as his power of language faded with the loss of the gem, his last cogent thought being, 'I must get home!'"

Suddenly, Josiah cawed and Lucy shrieked, startling Vladimir so much that he spilled his tea onto his lap. He squealed and jumped to his feet, bellowing, "What in Langdimania's name is wrong with you animals?"

He looked at his friends and saw them staring past him to the far end of the room where he could just make out, like something glimpsed from the corner of one's eye, a vanishing image of the boy sitting on the red sofa.

"A ghost!" Lucy said, as the vision faded completely from view.

"No, not a ghost, Lucy, it was him!" cried Josiah.

"You mean…" Lucy stuttered, and went silent.

"The Third Visitation," Josiah and Vladimir said together in awe.

Vladimir came to life, switched gears, became his Patternologist self, and immediately started interrogating the witnesses, his friends. "Tell me *exactly* what you just saw," he said, "and don't leave out a thing."

"There's nothing to describe, Vladimir," Josiah began. "He appeared for just a moment, sitting on the couch with his head drooping forward and his eyes closed, as if he were falling asleep, and then he looked startled and… poof! Gone."

And then the ever-observant Lucy added, "And he had one hand in his pocket."

Vladimir wrote it all down on his scroll and muttered, "We didn't notice the lights because we were entranced by the fire."

Lucy asked, "What do we do now, Vladimir?"

Vladimir considered the question, took a deep breath, and then answered it in line with the principles of Patternology. "We continue as we were. We remain in control of the experiment. We don't change a thing, back to the story!"

"Well, in that case, I'll brew another pot of tea," said Lucy.

CHAPTER 23

Army's first afternoon class after lunch was science
taught by Mr Rupoli. Army liked the class and his
teacher. Mr Rupoli was a funny, slightly overweight
man, given to wearing tan suit jackets and plaid wool ties.
He always taught in a very energetic manner that quite often
left him red in the face. Army thought he looked a bit like
a dish of ice cream with a large strawberry on top.

Mr Rupoli's classroom was probably the most
interesting one in the whole school. He had all sorts of
fascinating objects stacked on the shelves lined up along the
walls. There were telescopes, microscopes, and
gyroscopes. There were triple-beam balance scales and
racks of test tubes. There were gerbil cages, guinea pig
cages, and fish tanks. But best of all there was Cookie the
monkey. A real, live capuchin monkey! It was hard not to
love Mr Rupoli's class and Army always looked forward to
it. However, on this particular day, Army was too distracted
by what had happened in the library during recess and he
was dying to see what was in the envelope that fell out of
the mysterious book.

Mr Rupoli started the class off by saying that they were
going to be learning about the animals of the Serengeti in
Sub-Saharan Africa, including elephants, giraffes, and

lions. He then held up a giant map of Africa and proceeded to explain where the Serengeti was, its climate, and some of the various animals the children would be familiar with that came from there. All very interesting, of course, but not as much so to Army as the envelope in his back pocket. With his classmates distracted by Mr Rupoli's presentation, Army took the opportunity to take out the envelope, hold it under his desk, and open it up. Inside was a very old, folded up piece of paper and, as he slid it out, he got a faint whiff of cedar and almond rising from it. Army looked up and saw that everyone was staring ahead at the teacher. Looking back down and slouching a bit in his chair to be as unnoticeable as possible, Army unfolded the paper and was stunned by what he saw. It was a map, but not just any map. It was a map of Langdimania! His Langdimania! The maps he had been drawing for the last few weeks. The fantasyland he was king of. But he hadn't drawn this map. Was this a prank? Was Mike pranking him?

Army looked over at Mike sitting across the aisle. It had to be him. Army hadn't shown the maps to anyone else. But how did Mike know to put it in the exact book that Army would look through? Or maybe he hadn't! Maybe he followed Army, was hiding in the library behind the book return cart and had thrown the envelope to the floor so it just *looked* like it fell out of the book. Army had to know.

"Nice one, Mike," Army whispered.

Mike turned and looked at his friend.

"What?" he said.

"The map. I know it was you."

"What map? What are you talking about?"

"The map in the library," Army replied, his whisper growing louder in frustration, "the one in the envelope you dropped."

"I have no idea what you're talking about," Mike whispered back, while furtively keeping an eye on Mr Rupoli who was now looking their way.

"Yeah, right," Army hissed as he held the map up for Mike to see, "like you didn't draw this!"

"What's going on back there?"

Oh no! It was Mr Rupoli!

"Army? Mike? I don't think you're discussing the fauna of Africa, are you?" the science teacher said, as he walked over to their desks.

Army and Mike froze, ironically just the way that a gazelle does when spotted by a leopard, as Mr Rupoli had just been discussing.

"Is this what you boys were whispering about?" Mr Rupoli asked as he took hold of the paper that Army was still holding up to Mike. Army instinctively gripped harder onto the old map until he saw the serious way his teacher was glaring at him, and then he released it with a sigh.

"I'll hold onto this," Mr Rupoli insisted. "You can have it back at end of the term. That should keep you paying attention from now on."

Mr Rupoli headed back up to the front of the room, giving Army time to stick his tongue out at Mike, who just replied by mouthing the words, "It wasn't me."

The class lecture continued but, contrary to the teacher's hopes, Army was paying even less attention to it than before. If Mike hadn't drawn the map than who did? Army just *had* to get that map back. Mr Rupoli turned off the lights and started showing the class a movie on the animals of the sub-Saharan. Army sat steaming in his chair, watching the images of giraffes and hippopotami flow by while he fiddled with The Langdim Finder in his pocket. He was trying to figure out a way to distract the teacher and his class enough so that he could get into the desk drawer where Mr Rupoli kept the various items he forced students to relinquish over the school year.

"If only the fire alarm went off or the projector blew up." Army thought while randomly depressing buttons on his toy.

And then on the screen a lion appeared; a big, handsome lion with a full mane, basking in the sun on the savannah. From the back of the room, Cookie the monkey started chattering away as the camera zoomed up to the lion and the narrator intoned, "And so we come to the lion; the king of the jungle. Just listen to him roar and you'll know why he's called the king." The camera got really close up and the lion filled the screen. Cookie started jumping about and chattering louder and more rapidly. The lion opened his huge mouth and let out a terrifying roar. It was at this point that chaos took over the room, for Cookie thought that the lion was real and he had gotten so frightened when it roared that he let out a screech, followed by a long string of yellow pee that arced into the air and straight down the back of the dress of Nan, the poor unfortunate girl sitting in the back row. Nan turned around and, realizing what had just happened, let out an ear-shattering shriek which caused Cookie to scream louder as well, and the class went absolutely bonkers. Mr Rupoli ran to the back of the room to calm everything down and that's when Army seized his chance. He ducked down and ran up to the front of the room to his teacher's desk. He flew open the drawer of forbidden items and there was his map laying on top of assorted water pistols, Pokémon cards, yo-yos, and packages of gum. He grabbed his prize and scurried back to his seat just as the lights came back on and Nan ran crying out of the room with the best and worst excuse for leaving school early that anybody ever had. Mr Rupoli placed a big blanket over Cookie's cage and the animal calmed down, only letting out the occasional chirping noise.

"All right class. All right, everyone settle down. That's enough excitement for one day," Mr Rupoli announced. "Now open your science books to the start of chapter three and read quietly to yourselves until the bell."

With his map safely back in his pocket, Army didn't want to do anything else to draw attention to himself, so he opened his book along with the rest of his class and began to read about the strange beasts of Africa.

CHAPTER 24

Settled in with his freshly steeped second cup of black peppermint tea, Vladimir returned to the telling of The Story.

"As he flew back home, Joseph's power of reasoning faded until all he was left with was a vague, despondent feeling of emptiness and grief. When he arrived in his tree the other birds glanced at him as one would at a wedding guest, trying to remember if they'd been invited or not. Joseph roosted, tucked his head beneath his wing, and fell into a restless sleep, dreaming of bulls crushing glittering stones to dust beneath their charging hooves.

"Meanwhile, a wonderful, miraculous thing was happening. The Langdim Finder had settled onto the F'arm riverbed a few feet from the shore. The rays of the sun passing through the water reflected off of the stone, casting dancing prismatic reflections across the faces of the thirsting animals. Now, some say it was the light hitting them, while others say it was the drinking of the water, but one by one each creature began to think in words! And, like with the crows, as one animal gained the knowledge the rest of their clan did so as well through a kind of morphic resonance. The first to speak was a sheep who had accidentally pushed past a horse and, not wanting to cause offense, said, 'I'm sorry.'

'Oh no, no,' replied the horse, 'there's enough for everyone. Please drink.'

"As each animal gained the ability to verbalize, they turned to their neighbors and greeted them. A warm, loving atmosphere enveloped the creatures of F'arm as they began to express feelings that had always lain hidden behind the dull alarm bells of their fight or flight reflexes. After much conversation and laughter they decided to go to the crow's tree to thank Joseph, knowing now that it must have been a gift from him and the crows.

"A delegation was chosen, representing members of the newly enlightened species. A small parade - consisting of a sheep, a horse, a pig, a cow, a bull, and a dog - left the river and walked over the fields to find Joseph. When they got to his tree, they called to him. However, the shoe was now on the other foot and Joseph and the crows didn't understand the racket coming up at them from the ground below. They were startled by the commotion and, as one, they took to the skies. Up they flew once more, circling like a black tornado above the now terrified delegation below.

'This is crazy, they're attacking again!' whinnied the horse (at this point the new animals did not yet have names).

'Run for it!' barked the dog.

"And off they ran back to the watering place, while above them flew the crows, diving and dodging through the sky. Once back with the other animals, the small contingent quickly explained that the crows didn't have language and were on the warpath. Once again, a great fear swept over the crowd. One crow is bother enough, but the entire murder of crows was a great danger indeed!"

At this point in the story, even though they'd heard it hundreds of times before, Josiah and Lucy leaned in to hear every word, anticipating each twist in the tale.

Vladimir continued, "The crows circled through the kaleidoscopic air above the gathering at the river and, as they did so, the veils in their minds lifted and they could understand words again!

'I can think again! I can speak again!' cried one bird.

'Me too!' cried another.

'And me!' sounded yet another.

"Suddenly, Joseph recalled the charge of the bulls and how his entire flock could have been wiped out. He remembered his arrogance; he remembered the chaos. What if the beasts of F'orest got hold of the gem? If they ever organized and attacked, they'd overwhelm F'arm in mere minutes. The jewel was too dangerous and so he decided to rid his world of the stone once and for all. He flew at frightening speed towards the water and this time, with his faculties fully intact, he finally spotted the gem. Now, crows aren't waterfowl and can't swim, but they are, as we know (and with this Vladimir paused and smiled at Josiah), very smart and can use tools. And so, Joseph landed, grabbed a stick from the ground, and used it to push the bauble close enough for him to grab it in his beak and fly off again towards the mysterious well at the eastern edge of F'arm. No-one knows who built it, but even before we had language, we knew that it was something to be reckoned with. Bottomless and, dare I say it, infinite. It's puzzled me my whole life, always shrouded in a dark fog as if light itself was drowning in it.

93

"Joseph hovered above the never-ending hole and dropped what we now call The Langdim Finder into it, watching its last sparkle snuff out as it fell into the swirling abyss."

Vladimir paused and turning to Lucy said, "Perhaps there are some biscuits in the cupboard, my dear?"

CHAPTER 25

For the remainder of the school day, Army was pretty much left on his own. The whole 'Cookie The Monkey Incident' had taken the number one spot on the 'Top Ten Most Embarrassing Things To Happen To A Kid In School' list, replacing Army's outburst the day before on the school bus and giving him a bit of a breathing space from public ridicule, though he still had a lingering feeling that he was being watched.

In any case, Army had plenty of time to ponder the old map and its meaning. He didn't dare examine it in school again; that would have to wait until he was safely back home in his room. However, he couldn't help but ponder the implications of the map's appearance. If Mike didn't plant it for him to find, then who did? Willie knew about The Langdim Finder but he hadn't ever seen the maps of Langdimania that Army had sketched out. Could someone else be taunting him? The map felt like a ticking time bomb in his pocket, ticking faster and faster as the classroom clocks seemed to do just the opposite, ticking slower and slower toward the day's end. His anxiety went on uninterrupted until he was walking down the hallway toward English class. Finally, the last class of the day! He was almost free, but then he once again had a strange feeling of being observed. He whipped around and thought he saw a shadowy figure duck behind a classroom door. He started towards it to see who had been spying on him, when he was suddenly confronted by Cathy.

"Hello Army," she said, "I didn't see you on the bus to school today."

"Yeah, well, my usual seat was taken," Army lied, trying to get past her.

"Well, I was looking for you to see if you were serious yesterday," Cathy countered, not giving an inch.

"It's none of your business," Army growled as he realized he'd missed his quarry.

Army didn't want to talk about his outburst of affection for Wendy and, seeing that he was only about a dozen lockers away from his class, he dodged around Cathy and continued briskly on.

Cathy trotted along beside him to keep up and said, "I mean, about not trying out for the school musical."

Army just glared at her, but she kept on talking anyway. "I hear it's going to be The Wizard of Oz." She paused and winked at Army as she continued, "and Wendy's trying out for Dorothy." And with that she brushed past him into the classroom. Army followed her in and headed over to his seat by the window. Mr Fulmar, the English teacher, was just beginning the day's lesson so the class settled quickly. Army took a quick, surreptitious glance towards the middle desks and saw Cathy and Wendy once again whispering and looking at him as the class quieted down into silence.

Army hunched down in his chair with his hands in his sweatshirt pockets and focused his attention outside the classroom window while he played with The Langdim Finder. Even before he had gotten the toy, Army had a neat trick for times like this when he just wanted to disappear. He usually employed it in Mr Dumont's class to escape the tedium. He liked English class and Mr Fulmar but on days like this when all he wanted to do was to escape back home to his bedroom so that he could study the strange map far from the spying eyes of classmates like Cathy and Wendy, on days like this Army employed his trick. He would focus his attention on the topmost point of one of the pine trees that bordered the school grounds. He'd then concentrate hard and imagine that he was sending his consciousness out to that tippy point. He'd focus so hard that he could almost feel that he had risen out of his body, floated through the window, and was standing on top of the fir tree, looking laughingly back at the school, and at himself sitting at his desk staring back out at him. From there, he could turn around and fly wherever he pleased until the school bell rang or, as was more often the case, until Mr Dumont whacked his desk with the ruler and brought him back into his body.

This time was different though for, as he concentrated and projected himself onto the astral plane, he was simultaneously pushing the buttons of The Langdim Finder, and the fluorescent lights of the classroom began the now familiar flickering. Army wasn't startled like before. Instead, he allowed himself to enjoy the feeling. The flickering became flashing but no one in the room took any notice. Army took one last look back at Wendy and then he vanished, only to reappear, not on top of the tree, but on Vladimir's sofa in the Tower of Patterns.

CHAPTER 26

Vladimir settled back into his straw with a nice mound of butter cookies while Josiah happily pecked at a macaroon on his perch and Lucy discreetly munched on a biscotti. The fire had died down considerably and was now merely a rolling pulsation of dark oranges and glowing reds peeking through blackened logs and grey ash.

Vladimir washed down his third biscuit with a gulp of tea and continued on, "Well, that's it really. Joseph flew back to F'arm River to find that all the animals who'd been affected by the rainbow waters had retained the power of speech, and to this day so do all of their descendants."

Here he ended the tale, stared into the dwindling fire, and picked up another buttery delight.

"You know full well that isn't the end of the story, Vladimir," Josiah pointed out. "What about the Floating Girl?"

"Yes, Vladimir, tell us about The Girl, it's my favorite part even though it's so sad," Lucy begged.

"I'm all talked out for now. Lucy, why don't you pick it up from here, as is traditional," said Vladimir.

"Okay then," Lucy agreed and, after a sip of tea, she began. "Many stories went by after Joseph dropped the language maker down The Wishing Well, a full history of which can wait for another day. Suffice to say that the animals of F'arm grew wise, named all things, and lived good and happy lives, only occasionally and tragically interrupted by a stray beast from F'orest who made it past the barrier of the bulls. But what concerns us now is the day The Floating Girl appeared in The Wishing Well.

"It was a lovely spring day. The last snows of winter had come and gone leaving only a few frosty chunks of ice glittering and melting in the morning sunshine. Three young lambs had wandered from the flock and were quietly grazing near The Wishing Well when they were startled by a voice coming from the depths.

'Where am I? What's happening? Oh, goodness gracious!' it cried.

"The frightened lambs ran back to the flock and told the mistress sheep, Eloise, what had happened. She chided them for making up fairy stories but they were insistent that she go look. To placate the children and get back to the important tasks of grazing, napping, and then grazing again, Eloise trotted with them over to The Wishing Well and saw nothing unusual.

'Well?' she began to say to the lambs before she was interrupted by a voice coming from The Wishing Well.

'Well? Yes! I'm in a well!' the mysterious voice cried out.

"The very surprised Eloise stood up on her hind legs and peered over The Wishing Well's wall and there she saw what we later learned was a creature called 'a human,' and a young female one at that. Frightened by this apparition, Eloise herded the lambs together and they raced down the hill to join the rest of the flock and consult with Master Jenkins, the chief ram.

"Once again a procession went up the rise, this time led by Master Jenkins followed by a few others from the ram council. Jenkins approached The Wishing Well, clambered to get a good footing on the wall, and peered down. And there he saw the new creature standing on a short protuberance of rock and clinging to the sides of the shaft. She looked frightened and that emboldened Jenkins to enquire, 'Are you OK?'

'Did you just talk?' the girl asked."

Josiah interrupted excitedly, "Just like The Arrival when he asked if you talked, Vladimir!"

Vladimir replied, "Yes, indeed. Keep going Lucy, let's see if any other patterns emerge."

Lucy nodded and continued, "Master Jenkins shouted down The Wishing Well, 'Of course I talked. You don't see anyone else here do you?'

'No, I guess not,' the girl replied. 'It's just that I've never heard a goat talk before.'

'A goat?' exclaimed Jenkins. 'I'm not a goat. I'm a ram!'"

Lucy lowered her voice, interrupting her narrative in order to comment to her friends, "Rams are not famous for having even tempers, are they?" Vladimir and Josiah nodded hurriedly, both recalling unfortunate instances of being on the wrong end of a ram's temper.

Lucy continued, "'Oh, I'm sorry,' the girl replied in a fearful voice, for Jenkins' temper, on top of the fact that she had suddenly appeared on a precarious foothold, had her quite shaken up.

'Well, you should be!' Jenkins harrumphed. 'And what are you supposed to be anyway?'

'Why, I'm a girl!'

'Yes, yes, but a girl what?'

'What do you mean?'

'Well,' Jenkins replied impatiently, 'are you a girl rabbit or a girl mole? Or some other type of girl that hides in holes?'

'I'm just a girl girl, I suppose. Please, do you think you could help me get out of here?'

"Brought back to the seriousness of the situation, Jenkins blinked and replied, 'Of course, hold on and I'll bring help.'

"Jenkins dropped back to the ground and turning around he was taken aback to suddenly find himself facing a huge crowd of creatures from F'arm. It seemed the wind had whispered the news to the trees who then told the birds who told everyone else and they had all come out to see what was in The Wishing Well.

'It's – it's,' he stammered at them, 'it's a girl girl!'

"The animals responded with whoops and cheers, thinking that Master Jenkins was announcing a newborn lamb. Three other rams charged him and butted his head to congratulate him. He was so dazed by the crowd and the whacks to his noggin that it took him quite a while to quiet everyone down.

'Listen to me!' he shouted, 'Listen! I'm not a dad!'

'What are you talking about, you old dodger?' asked William, one of the larger horses.

'Yeah,' rejoined Copernicus, an elder pig, 'you announced a girl!'

'Yes,' replied the flustered Master Jenkins, 'a girl, but not a girl lamb…'

'Then a girl what?' said William.

'In The Wishing Well. See for yourself,' Jenkins said.

"The animals rushed to The Wishing Well and the horses and several crows peered over the edge and looked down. There they saw The Girl looking back up at them. One of the crows, a young female crow named Betty, cried down to the girl, 'Who are you?'

'It's about time someone asked me that. I'm Wendy and I'd really like some help getting out of this well!'"

CHAPTER 27

A rmy jumped to his feet to take in all the sights and sounds of where he was as quickly as he could. He had no idea how long he'd be there before being whisked back to Mr Fulmar's English class. The room had a familiarity to it this time as if he was in a dream he had dreamed before. A dream déjà vu perhaps? Behind him was the ornate red couch he had materialized upon last time, and before him was a raised platform holding an amazingly impressive desk. Beyond that he could see three very curious animals, their eyes wide in amazement, all sitting very still and staring intently at him. A sheep had now joined the pig and the crow that he had seen before, and they looked like statues posed in the middle of sipping cups of tea. Did they think they were hiding? The glowing fireplace, casting dim dancing shadows across the tableau, was the only indication that time itself hadn't come to a full stop.

The moment ended when Lucy finally spoke up, "I supposed then that you'll be surprised to learn that I can talk?"

Army's mouth hung open but he was speechless. Slowly, he sat back down.

"And apparently, he can't," Josiah grinned (not so much with his mouth which was, of course, a hard beak, but with his eyes and a slight tilt of his head.)

"I – I – I," Army began, "I mean, you – you – you…"

"Oh dear," Lucy remarked, "you are having a hard time of it, aren't you? Perhaps a nice cup of black peppermint tea is in order."

Lucy got up to put the kettle to boil. The naturalness of the act served to calm Army's nerves a bit, and so he finally asked, "Where am I?"

Vladimir very slowly lowered his cup to his lap and replied, "Specifically, you're sitting on a couch in my Patternology tower. Generally, and more expansively, you're in the land of F'arm in the dimension of Langdimania."

"Langdimania!" Army repeated in astonishment. "Then this *must* be a dream."

"Funny," Josiah recalled, "that's exactly what The Floating Girl said. Another sign, Vladimir!"

"Yes, Josiah, already noted," Vladimir responded carefully in order to keep the emotions in the room reined in, and then, once again speaking to Army, he continued in as nonchalant a tone as he could muster, "and yes, Langdimania in general, and in F'arm, specifically. Why don't you join us over here by the fire?"

"Really," Josiah said haughtily, "where else in Langdimania would he arrive, F'orest?"

Vladimir shot Josiah a glare and then returned as quickly as possible to smiling towards Army.

Army hesitated.

"Oh shush, Josiah," Lucy interjected, "he's obviously not in F'orest. Why would he ever go there?" Then, putting the kettle on its heater, she turned encouragingly to Army, "It's perfectly okay. We're just having tea and telling stories."

Comforted once more by the sheep's tender manner, and figuring that it was all just a dream and he'd be waking up soon anyway, Army stood up and walked over to the beckoning animals. They smiled and welcomed him to their circle.

"I have so many questions," Army began.

"So do we!" Josiah said, bouncing excitedly on his perch.

"It's interesting that you've appeared here again just as the girl in our story did," observed Vladimir.

"Girl? What girl?" asked Army, as he took a seat on a low wooden bench topped with a dark blue cushion.

"The other human who's visited here. The one who signified your arrival," Vladimir replied.

"She appeared in The Wishing Well," Lucy said, feeling very pleased to finally meet The Arrival. "I was just telling about that bit."

"I don't understand what you're talking about," Army responded.

"It's simple really," said Josiah. "You're not the first human to visit us. The Girl was, if you don't count The Ancients. It's such a shame that she froze. I hope it doesn't happen to you too."

"Froze?" Army said, trying to keep down a sense of panic that the dream was turning in a bad direction.

"Josiah, please," cautioned Vladimir.

"Now don't get excited," Josiah said. "She's still alive... we think."

"What?" cried Army.

"Hush Josiah, you're just making it worse," Lucy said.

Vladimir turned back to Army and said in a voice as gently as he could (which for Vladimir sounded more like a low grumble), "She's not frozen in a cold, icy, sense. She's just, ahem, stuck."

"And floating," Josiah added.

Army felt the familiar sensation of his face turning hot and his palms starting to sweat.

"Oh, you lot are just scaring him," Lucy interjected, trying to save the day. "The girl is not in any danger. She's not frozen or in harm's way. It's more like she's just waiting."

"Waiting for what? Where is she? Who is she?" Army questioned the animals before him. He was suddenly thrust into this drama about a mysterious girl, when mere minutes ago he had processing the talking animals, the tower, and how real the dream seemed.

"Well," said Vladimir, "as to the 'waiting for what' question, I am 93% sure that what she is waiting for is you. For the where question, she is floating in The Wishing Well. As for your third query, the who part, her name is Wendy, and now, may I ask, what is your name?"

"Wendy!" Army exclaimed and jumped to his feet. What were the odds?

"Your name is also Wendy?" Josiah asked startled.

"Do all of you creatures have the same name?" Lucy joined in.

"What? No. My name isn't Wendy!" Army explained hurriedly as he reached into his pocket and clasped The Langdim Finder. It was the one thing that seemed to exist in both his waking world and this phantasm of a place. It felt real and solid and he began pushing the buttons for reassurance. Thus emboldened, and in a fitful attempt to protect himself, but from what he wasn't sure, Army decided not to tell them his real name. "My name is Spitfire," he blurted out.

"Spitfire?" cried Josiah in alarm. "Are you a dragon?"

Army realized that his fake name was only increasing the confusion of the moment and he continued on, "No, no, I'm not a dragon. I'm Army!"

"His hand is in his pocket!" Lucy bleated.

"No!" Vladimir cried out.

Just then, the whistle on the kettle went off high and loud, and Army jumped a foot in the air it frightened him so. He squeezed The Langdim Finder with all of his might in alarm, and the lights began flashing on and off in rapid succession.

"Don't leave us! We need you; she needs you!" Lucy shouted.

"I was right all along; he is the Army!" exulted Vladimir.

"The Girl!" Josiah joined in. "You have to save Wendy!"

And just like that, Army disappeared from the tower. The high shrill of the teakettle whistle transformed into the ringing of the end of class bell as Army landed back in his body in Mr Fulmar's room, his head down on his desk as if he had passed out. He quickly lifted his head to see if anyone had noticed and was relieved to find that the class was moving along normally with no one paying any attention to him. That is, until his gaze hit the back of the room, where he saw Wendy staring intently at him while she gathered her books. She signaled Army to look back down at his desk. Army turned and saw that there was a note near where he had lain his head. He quickly picked up the note and unfolded it behind a shielding hand. The note contained only three words, but it's amazing how sometimes three little words can change your life.

CHAPTER 28

The note read, "Save me, Army!"

Army's thoughts raced.

"Save me?" Army wondered. "How does she know what I was dreaming?"

Army looked back up at Wendy to see that she was heading out with the rest of the students. He grabbed his books, stood up, checked his sweatshirt pocket for The Langdim Finder, and headed for the door to catch up with her.

"Army!" Mr Fulmar called after him.

Army turned around, wondering what fresh trouble he was in. Had Mr Fulmar caught him zoning out?

"Did you drop this?" Mr Fulmar asked, holding in his hand the envelope with the map in it.

"Uh, yes, Mr Fulmar," Army replied nervously.

"Well, here you go then," his teacher said, extending the envelope out to Army, "and if you need help, let me know."

"What?" Army said, slowly taking his envelope back.

"Help, Army. You're a really bright kid but lately you seem distracted. If there's anything you need to talk about, I'm here."

"Why yes, now that you mention it, there's these crazy animals in another world who want me to save Wendy from something but I don't understand what it is and just when I thought it was all a dream, Wendy left me a note asking me to save her! Does she mean in the other world or in the school play? What should I do?" is what Army wanted to say. But what he actually said was, "Um, thanks Mr Fulmar, but I'm fine."

"OK, but the offer's there, if you need my help."

"OK, sure thing," Army countered, saying anything he could to make his escape and try to catch up to Wendy, "I'll let you know. I've got to run or I'll miss the bus."

And then Army was out the door and running down the school hallway. When he got outside to where the buses were filling up with students going home, he saw Wendy and Cathy waving excitedly to him through their bus window. He wanted to speak with Wendy but he also wanted nothing to do with Cathy. Army jumped on a different bus that was just closing its doors and pulling out. This one dropped him off further from his house than his regular bus, but it'd be worth it to have a safer ride home.

As the bus drove along and Army settled into his seat, he thought of how his parents always asked him how school went each day. If only they knew!

CHAPTER 29

Josiah was saying, "I'm telling you, he knew who you were talking about. He knows The Girl. He knows Wendy."

"Josiah's right, Vladimir. Wendy isn't waiting for an army, she's waiting for this boy *named* Army," Lucy joined in, as she served yet another round of freshly brewed tea, this time with a tray of barley scones.

Vladimir nodded solemnly, "Yes, all signs would point to that conclusion."

Lucy continued, "So, what do we do now? How do we get him back?"

"And what's more," Josiah chimed back in, "how do we get him to save The Girl?"

Vladimir popped a whole scone in his mouth and munched away as he considered the situation. Josiah and Lucy nibbled at theirs, waiting to hear from their esteemed friend what the best course of action was. Finally, Vladimir spoke up, "We continue as before. We tell The Story."

"But Vladimir, old friend," Josiah said, "we already know The Story, we must take action!"

"Well, Josiah, what action would you propose we undertake?" Vladimir enquired.

"I don't know, gather a search party and seek him out?"

"But where would we look? Each time he's appeared he's come closer and closer to the story-fire. Have you noticed that? First in the field, then twice on the couch. But the last time he appeared, he actually joined us in the circle, at least until the mention of The Floating Girl and the sound of the kettle's whistle scared him off. He'll be back; he'll appear right here beside us, and he'll ask to hear more about The Girl."

When the High Patternologist spoke with such certainty, no one questioned him. Whether it was when the harvest would come in, when the next beast incursion was due, or what the wind was saying, Vladimir was invariably spot on with his predictions or close enough for supper[8].

Josiah looked at Lucy who looked back at him, then over to Vladimir, and said, "OK, then, I might as well take it from here. Put another log on the fire, Lucy, and I'll get started."

Lucy got up and fixed the fire so that it was once more a steady blaze.

"After the usual round of debate that apparently has to happen before anyone around here does anything," Josiah began, giving a sly look at Vladimir who scowled back at him, "the animals finally settled on a plan to get The Girl out of The Wishing Well. A long length of sheep's wool was gathered and fashioned into a harness and rope, and while it was being fashioned the animals kept The Girl's spirits up by taking turns talking to her. She seemed as fascinated by them as they were of her.

---

[8] "Close enough for supper" is a saying the animals of F'arm have. It means, "It'll do."

'How did you get in The Well?' they asked.

"Wendy laughed and replied, 'I fell asleep and awoke here in this silly dream.'

'This isn't a dream,' Daniel the crow informed her.

'That's exactly what a talking bird in a dream would say,' Wendy replied with self-satisfaction.

'Well,' Daniel retorted, 'I'd say a dream would be of a place where us birds *can't* talk. More of a nightmare, really.'

"Eventually the harness was lowered down. The Girl strapped it around herself and shouted up that she was ready to be pulled aloft. The other end of the rope had been tied to William the horse and, at Jenkins' signal, he slowly strode ahead with the rope becoming taut behind him.

"Daniel kept up the conversation, partly to calm The Girl's nerves and partly out of sheer curiosity.

'If this is all a dream - your dream - then where are you sleeping now?'

'In my bed, of course,' she answered, as she ever so carefully climbed the wall of The Wishing Well with William pulling her up.

'Yes, yes, I know that,' Daniel continued as he fluttered above her head, 'but where in Langdimania is your bed?'

'Langdimania?' The Girl cried out. 'Do you know…'

"Now some say it was a bee and others say it was a mouse and still others say it was the shout of The Girl (and the horses still refuse to talk about it to this day) but all of a sudden, William reared up on his hind legs and the rope went slack. The Girl screamed and the animals gasped, as if they had all been punched in the stomach at the same time. They charged towards The Wishing Well and stared down into the abyss, but The Girl was gone; only the fading echoes of her last exclamation remained, 'Army?'"

CHAPTER 30

Army arrived home just in time to help set the table for dinner, during which he was asked how school was that day and, as usual, he smiled and said it was fine. After dinner, he desperately wanted to run upstairs to examine the old map he'd found, but he watched a bit of TV with his parents first just so they wouldn't wonder why he hadn't. Eventually, his impatience got the better of him and he announced he was going to his room before the end of the show.

"A bit early for bedtime isn't it, Army?" his mom remarked.

"Well," Army replied, "I want to get a jump on my homework and I need to look some things up on my computer."

"OK then," Army's dad said. "I'll be up to check on you after we watch one more episode. I'm just addicted to this show!"

Army climbed the steps up to his bedroom; the laugh track of the sitcom his parents were watching faded into muffled tones, only to be replaced by the strident sounds emanating out of his brother's room of a sports announcer expressing amazement at a ball going over a wall. He thought for a second about going into Nick's room and

113

telling him what was happening, but he knew it would end with something being thrown at him followed by a yell to 'Get out'. Wincing at the imagined impact of an object hitting his head, he continued on into his own room. He went over to his computer desk, sat down, and began to investigate "suddenly understanding a foreign language". What he found startled him. He wasn't alone, well, not entirely. It seemed that there were numerous instances of people coming out of comas with the sudden knowledge of a foreign language!

"Just like me," Army thought, "except I don't think I was in a coma. But I *did* faint, didn't I? Those flashing lights and my passing out, dreaming of that other land with the castle and the talking animals, was that a coma? Do people in comas dream?"

He researched it and apparently the answer was yes; people do dream in comas. But then he realized that in Lorenzo's and Mr Wu's he wasn't *in* a coma. He had picked up Italian and Mandarin by utilizing The Langdim Finder. Or had he? Perhaps The Langdim Finder was merely a placebo and he only imagined that it gave him the powers that the coma had induced. It was all very confusing.

An experiment was in order. He took the envelope out of his pocket, opened it and carefully extracted the old map, unfolded it and placed it on his desk before him. There it was; Langdimania. A land he thought he had made up. An imaginary world he ruled. The fantasy that had lost him Wendy... or had it? He studied the various landmasses and waterways, the mountains and forests. Some names he recognized; names he had made up like Castle Island and the Negazone. There were also other names he didn't know, like Voidland and two areas, F'arm and F'orest, connected by a long, thin stretch of land.

"Wait a minute!" Army said aloud. "F'arm and F'orest. The pig had said that they lived in F'arm of Langdimania. That's it then. That's where I'll go."

Army took out The Langdim Finder and placed it on the map before him. He needed to know if it was responsible for his new talents or not. He needed to find out once and for all if he could visit Langdimania for real and on purpose. He needed proof. If only he could bring something from there back to here, to his real world bedroom. He picked up The Langdim Finder and started pushing the buttons while staring at the map.

Now, you know when you are supposed to be concentrating on one thing but something else that you are *not* supposed to be thinking about keeps getting in the way? In this case, Army kept trying to concentrate on F'arm as he manipulated The Langdim Finder but instead his thoughts kept drifting to Lucy the sheep saying, "He's obviously not in F'orest, why would he ever go there?"

Army kept trying to focus on the word F'arm on the map, but he couldn't help but also look at the land of F'orest and to repeat in his head, like a song that had gotten stuck on an infinite loop, "F'orest, why would he ever go there?"

And before he knew it, his bedroom lights did the now familiar strobe dance, faster and faster, until he blinked out of his room and reappeared hovering in a seated position two feet above the leaf-strewn, moonlit, slightly moist floor of F'orest. Those few feet of air between him and the ground instantly disappeared and he fell hard. Lying there, Army made a mental note that next time he'd start the interdimensional transition with his feet firmly on the ground, instead of seated in a chair that wouldn't be making the trip with him.

CHAPTER 31

The night before she handed the note to Army, Wendy woke up screaming and sat bolt upright. She feverishly patted her sheets and the wall next to her bed to make sure that they were solid and that she was no longer falling down an endless well.

"Not again, not again!" she cried, for this wasn't the first time she'd dreamt of The Wishing Well. She'd had the dream twice before. The first time was the night after she heard of Army's servant game in school, and she saw Mike and Debbie arguing over who was the boss. She dreamt that night that she was standing in complete darkness until far, far above her she sensed, more than saw, a circle of light. The second time she had the dream was the night after Army had presented her that ridiculous scroll. That night she'd dreamt that she was once again standing in darkness, but this time she started out closer to the circle of light above and she thought she could hear birds singing as she felt a slight breeze filtering down to her. This third time, tonight when she'd just woke up screaming, was a few nights later and she dreamt that she was only a few meters from the circle and she could tell that she was standing on a stone angling out of the wall of a well. You know the dream by now, meeting Jenkins the ram, getting into the harness, and falling back down into the darkness.

Wendy turned on her bedroom light, took a deep breath and let it out slowly. She was shaken up by the fall in the dream, but she was even more disturbed by the fact that she didn't escape The Wishing Well. She wanted to meet the talking animals, to see the world they were living in, and to get out of that cold, damp well!

Wendy looked at the clock on the nightstand beside her bed and sighed; four more hours until she had to get up for school. She wanted to go back to sleep, but how could she be sure what she'd dream next? What if she reentered the dream in the middle of the fall? She reached under her pillow and pulled out the sparkling stone she had found last week. She'd discovered it (or did it discover her?) in a strange puddle on her way home after school. The puddle was strange for three reasons. The first being that it was a beautiful sunny day and it hadn't been raining at all. Secondly, the puddle was perfectly round as if it were in a container. And thirdly, it didn't seem to reflect what was actually above it. Yes, the reflection was of the sky and trees, but it seemed to be of a brighter sky and different trees. When she thought she saw the reflection of a distant, large, black bird in the water, she turned and looked up and no bird could be seen!

"Very odd," Wendy had thought to herself, looking up at the birdless sky. And then, even odder, when she looked back at the puddle, the bird was once again reflected and it seemed to drop something that got bigger and bigger as if it were descending toward her. Wendy quickly looked back up but nothing was falling towards her and still there was no bird overhead. She immediately looked back into the

117

puddle and saw that the reflected object was a glittering jewel that, instead of falling into the puddle from above her - well, there really is no other way to put it - the stone was falling *up* out of the puddle and into the air right in front of her! Wendy reflexively grabbed it before it could fall back into the puddle and, she thought, back to wherever it came from. That night she'd had the first dream of The Wishing Well, though she didn't know then that it would be just the first dream and that more would follow.

Sitting up in her bed, Wendy cradled the stone in the palm of her hand and watched the rainbow colors glitter and dance inside its facets. The more she thought about it, the more she became convinced that there was a connection between this stone and her recurring dream.

"I wonder," Wendy mused to herself, "if maybe this is a wishing stone. Maybe the well in my dream is a wishing well and this is a stone from it. That would explain why I keep going back there in the dream. Maybe I'm supposed to put the stone back. Maybe that will free me!"

Wendy's heart started racing with excitement, which is the last thing one wants their heart to do when they are preparing to go back to sleep. She reached over, switched off her light, and settled back under her covers, clasping the stone in her hand. She calmed her breathing down and pictured being back in the well. She imagined herself floating out of it and exploring a magical land filled with friendly talking animals. Slowly but steadily, she fell back asleep and soon her imaginings acquired a solidity to them as once again she was in The Wishing Well, only this time she was floating out of it; levitating as if she was standing on a rising platform. Very near the top she could see it was almost sunset as orange clouds lay streaked against a blueberry sky. Wendy could hear a voice talking in that way that voices sound like when they are telling an oft-told tale. Wendy floated up higher until she was able to make out what the storyteller was saying. It was a fascinating tale of a crow acquiring the power of speech and how he lost it and then regained it again along with all the other animals, and how he eventually threw the cause of the magic down The Wishing Well.

Intrigued, Wendy barely noticed the sky turning a deeper purple in the twilight and the pale, full moon appearing through the clouds. She began to feel The Well turning colder and she desperately wanted to climb out and ask for a sweater or a shawl. Then, to her amazement, the storyteller began to talk about her! Wanting to get closer so that she could hear more clearly, Wendy concentrated hard and floated to just below the lip of the top of The Well but, frustratingly, she found she could go no further. It was like she was tethered to something at the bottom of the pit, as if she were a helium balloon on a string and that string was now pulled tight and she couldn't rise any higher. She stopped struggling and allowed herself to float in place as she listened to the end of the story being told just out of reach. Astonishingly, the story ended with the teller saying, "… we continue to tell this tale to each other on the nights of the full moon at the base of The Wishing Well, so as not to forget the girl who we failed and the army who will save her."

"The army who will save her?" Wendy remarked to herself and then, realizing they must have meant her Army, she exclaimed, "Army!" but, as she did so she lost her concentration and hence her ability to levitate, and just like before she fell back down The Well, so that it sounded to the startled animals above, once again, like, "Arrrrrmy!"

CHAPTER 32

Army immediately sensed that he had made a mistake as he looked around at the dark woods that surrounded him. It was like arriving in the middle of a horror movie where one's not sure what's going on, but one knows something really bad is about to happen. He wasn't, as he had hoped he would be, in the cozy, opulently appointed tower, drinking tea with the storytelling animals of the land of F'arm.

"This must be the forest or, as the map called it, F'orest," Army shuddered. "This doesn't feel warm and welcoming at all!"

As his eyes adjusted to the dark, Army looked around at the tall trees towering over him. He stood still and listened intently. He could hear the wind rustling the swaying treetops and fluttering the leaves on the ground. He could hear the sounds of the nighttime insects humming away like tiny cars left idling against the background whoosh of a far distant river. Then he jumped as he heard what he thought at first was a crying cat but then, as he got his breath back, realized was a bird calling somewhere in the branches above.

Army didn't like F'orest from the moment he arrived there and he disliked it even more so now that he'd been there for a whole three minutes. He reached into his pocket for The Langdim Finder to jump home, but it was gone! It must have fallen out of his pocket when he hit the ground! His panic growing, Army searched frantically for The Finder. Things never seem to fall where you think they should. How many times in the past had he dropped a coin or a pen and went to look for where he thought it should be, only to find it on the opposite side of the room under something he hadn't expected? This looked like the case again as he didn't see a sign of The Finder anywhere.

Army heard a low growl. He froze in fear and once again wondered if this place used the 'wanted statues' like in his playtime fantasies. Even if they did, whatever was growling didn't seem to be the type of creature easily tricked or delayed by such a tactic. "Maybe," he thought frenetically, "I should run, or play dead, or climb one of the trees."

But for all Army knew, the thing lurking in the woods loved a good chase, was an expert at determining if something was dead, and excelled at climbing trees. As is so often the case while debating multiple courses of action to oneself, what Army actually did was nothing but what he had been doing, standing stock still on high alert.

He heard the growl again. It was clearly coming from his left. He twisted his head around and peered intently into the darkness from where it had emanated. That's when Army found out that the only thing worse than not being able to see a mysterious, snarling beast in the night is, instead, to be able to just make out its horrible, glowing green eyes and alarmingly large fangs.

Army's heart was in his throat as he prepared to feel the sharp rending of claws, when suddenly he saw it. The Langdim Finder was there, half buried in the dirt and halfway between himself and what was turning out to be a wild panther! There was no way he could get to the little satellite before the jungle cat got to him.

Precipitously, an idea popped into Army's head. Of course! The animals here speak! Maybe Army could convince the panther that he meant no harm, tasted awful, and just wanted to go home.

Army cleared his throat, which had grown thick with fear, and squeaked out, "Um, excuse me, Mr Panther sir. I'm Army. I just want…"

The terrifying roar of the panther cut Army off mid-sentence.

"OK," Army gulped in terror, "that was totally not English but it still needed no translation. Perhaps I only understand animals when I'm actually holding The Langdim Finder."

There was nothing for it then. Army would definitely get caught if he tried running away but he was a sitting duck staying where he was. His only chance was to dive for The Finder and hope that he could activate it before the animal attacked. Oh, and this was all assuming that the thing would work and save him.

Army counted to three and then sprang forward, running and then diving toward The Langdim Finder. The panther bellowed again, arched its back, and prepared for what it perceived as an assault, not realizing that Army was not attacking it, but going for the prize in the dirt instead. Army scooped The Finder up and tumbled to his right, away from the big cat. Seeing Army in retreat, the wild beast prepared to give chase, stalking forward from the bushes into the clearing with Army. Feverishly, Army began pushing the buttons and, because the school musical had been on his mind, he instinctively repeated out loud, "There's no place like home. There's no place like home."

"You're strange and I wonder what you taste like," the panther interrupted.

"What? You can speak?" Army cried out and then continued, "Please don't eat me!"

The panther slowly circled Army.

"What's going on?" the panther growled.

"What do you mean?"

"How is it that I am knowing you?"

Army wasn't sure what the panther meant but tried his best to respond, "You see me. I'm not here to fight you."

"As if you could!" roared the panther. Army was scared for his life and at his wit's end as to what to do next.

"I just want to go home!" Army stammered, unable to focus his attention on where home was so that he could activate a jump. The conversing feline monster was too distracting.

"Home? Where is home? Are there more of you? What do you taste like?"

The panther's growl had gained a hint of an evil purr to it as he attempted to ferret out where more prey like Army might be hiding.

"Oh, I taste horrible! I haven't bathed in days!" Army said quickly, while making a mental note that the next time his mother yelled at him for not taking a bath he could explain to her how good that is at keeping hungry panthers at bay.

The panther stopped his pacing and sat almost regally in front of Army.

"Tell me what you are and where others like you can be found and maybe I'll let you go," the panther said, unable to avoid looking and sounding like a cat playing with his food before devouring it.

Army realized he wasn't going to talk his way out of the dire situation he was in but, perhaps, if he kept the cat talking long enough instead of pouncing on him, he could concentrate again on vanishing back to his room. Once again, he started pushing the buttons on The Langdim Finder.

"Well, I'm a human boy and, as for where the others are, sure, I can tell you. We live at 18 Cherry Lane. 18 Cherry Lane." Army pictured his house at 18 Cherry Lane and pushed the buttons harder and faster. "Do you know where 18 Cherry Lane is? Oh boy, wait until you've visited 18 Cherry Lane."

The moon above them suddenly went out, vanished from the sky along with the stars, and they were blanketed in darkness. Pitch black except for the still glowing, emerald eyes of the startled panther.

"Where's the light?" the panther wondered out loud. "What happened to the glittering in the sky?"

And then the celestial bodies were turned back on again.

Army knew it was the start of a teleporting jump and he continued his button pushing and said rapidly, "Wow, yeah, look at that. That happens all the time at 18 Cherry Lane. 18 Cherry Lane! 18 CHERRY LANE!!!"

The night sky began to alternate off and on like a million fireflies blinking in unison until, suddenly, Army vanished from the forest clearing. As soon as he was gone, everything went back to normal. The moon shone its whitish grey smile, the stars twinkled, and a very bewildered panther rumbled to itself, "I must find this place he called… he called…" and then his words became a low growl as he lost the use of language along with his prey.

CHAPTER 33

L ucy said, "But not forgotten," with a smile.

"No, most definitely not," Josiah agreed and then, returning to the tale, he continued, "The animals remained on the lookout at The Well until sunrise the next day. Horses, dogs, crows, and rams all took turns keeping watch; sunup, sun in the center of the sky, and sundown. As one shift ended and another began, they'd wish each other a good watch along with good wishes for the return of the girl and so, eventually, it became known as The Wishing Well, and to this day, when departing each other's company, we wish each other well."

"Hear, hear," Lucy and Vladimir intoned together, as was the custom at this point in the tale, for there was only a little left to tell.

"And so it was and so it is," Josiah replied in the traditional manner, "that we continue to tell this tale to each other on the nights of the full moon at the base of The Wishing Well, so as not to forget the girl who we failed and the army who will save her."

And thus the tale was told, and with its finish a stillness filled the room as the animals stared into the dying embers' silent, pulsing glow, only occasionally interrupted by a spark's brief leap into the air.

Finally, as if recalling a dream, Vladimir spoke, "And so the story ends. The animals still fruitlessly guard The Wishing Well and I still make my useless predictions."

"That's a bit harsh," Josiah remarked.

"Yes, Vladimir, your predictions have not been useless. You predicted The Arrival and it *did* happen."

"Did it?" snorted Vladimir. "Did it really? I predicted an army; an army that would rescue The Girl and help protect us from the beasts of F'orest. And what did we get? A scared child who can't stay in the same place for more than a few minutes at a time!"

CHAPTER 34

Army found himself standing in the center of his bedroom at 18 Cherry Lane wildly pushing the buttons of his magical device.

"It worked!" he said breathlessly, as he fell back on his bed. "It really worked!"

Army laughed, half out of relief to be home and away from the claws of the panther, and half out of wonder that it all actually happened. It all did actually happen, didn't it?

Army looked at his chair by the desk where he had been sitting before he disappeared. He left from there but was standing in the middle of his room when he arrived back. People in comas don't move, right?

Army leaped back up and went over to his computer to look it up. A quick bit of research told him two things. First, no, people in comas don't move. That was good. Not a coma. Second, he forgot about sleepwalking, or somnambulism as he learned it was also called. He could've been sleepwalking. That would explain his arriving back in a different place than he left, like in detention and now again in his bedroom.

"I would need to bring something back from Langdimania to prove I was there," Army thought to himself. Then he had an idea. He had been rolling around the floor of the forest. He must have leaves, pine needles, or sticks stuck to him somewhere. He looked down at his clothes but they seemed untouched by his trip. He looked at himself in the full-length mirror that hung on the back of his door. Nothing. Not a leaf or a twig.

"This is ridiculous," he thought, "something must have stuck to me."

Army whipped off his jacket and checked his shirt. Nothing. He then took all of his clothes off, laid them out on his bed, and turned on all the lights of his room so he could look at them for evidence.

This is how a few minutes later when his dad walked in, he found Army in his underpants on his bed examining his clothes with a magnifying glass.

"Army!" his dad exclaimed. "What in heaven's name are you doing?"

Army jumped and, because of the bounciness of the bed, he flew up into the air and landed in a heap on the floor along with his discarded outfit.

"I'm, um, just making sure my clothes are clean for school tomorrow," Army said feebly.

"OK, whatever you say," Army's father said, not wanting to cause his son, or himself, any further embarrassment. "Just get into your pajamas and get to sleep then."

Mr Armstrong gave Army a reassuring smile and left to rejoin his wife in the television room.

Army got up and put his clothes away. There was no evidence that he had been to Langdimania anywhere on them. He'd just have to find another way, but he'd had enough for one night. His encounter with the panther had left him exhausted and so he put on his nightclothes and clambered into bed. He was asleep even as his head hit the pillow.

CHAPTER 35

The next morning, Army got dressed quickly. He tucked The Langdim Finder, as was now his usual habit, into his brown sweatshirt pocket, went downstairs to the kitchen for breakfast, and found his parents already there at the table talking quietly to each other. When Army came into the room they turned to face him with concerned expressions on their faces. Army stared back, wondering what was up, until he remembered the compromising position he had been discovered in the night before.

"Oh no," Army thought to himself, "I'm going to get a 'we must talk' lecture."

His parent's expressions then changed slowly and simultaneously from ones of parental worry to the weak smiles that are often displayed to cover up contrary emotions.

"OK," Army continued with his inner narrative, "this is getting a bit creepy."

"Good morning, Army," his mother said in a slightly singsong manner.

"Er, yes," his father agreed, "good morning son. Everything OK?"

Oh god. This was going to be torture.

"Yep," Army replied, as he quickly prepared a breakfast of cereal, milk, and sliced bananas. He then continued in the "nothing wrong here" manner that his parents were promulgating, "Everything's fine. See, my clothes from yesterday are still clean. We're learning about recycling and reusing in school and so I thought if I kept my clothes clean there'd be less to wash, and we'd save energy and the environment."

Wow, he thought that one up quick! And his parents seemed happy with the explanation.

"That's nice dear," his mother said.

"Good for you, son," his dad chimed in.

Army downed his breakfast and told his parents he wanted to make sure he didn't miss the bus. He dumped his bowl in the sink, gave his mom a peck on the cheek, and ran out the door.

"That wasn't *too* weird," Army said sarcastically to himself as he headed to school. The bus was just pulling up and so Army had to run the last twenty yards to his bus stop to make sure he got on. Between his pondering what was up with his parents and being glad to not miss the bus, Army totally forgot that Wendy and Cathy would be on board.

Out of breath and distracted, Army plopped down into his usual seat next to Willie. The bus resumed its daily drive to school.

"Hey Army, chancing the bus again?" Willie kidded his classmate.

Army turned towards Willie to reply, but the bright morning sun coming through the windows was dazzling and he had to shield his eyes, giving Willie a chance to continue to chide him.

"I mean, 'you-know-who' are in the back."

Army shrugged. He was too overwhelmed by everything going on to care; the breakfast he just had with his parents, last night's encounter with the panther, and now this blinding sun.

"Yeah, yeah, I know. Cathy and…" Army began but Willie interrupted him before he could finish.

"Wendy," Willie said.

"Yeah, that's who I was going to say, Wendy."

"No, Wendy," Willie repeated, deliberately using his eyes to signal to Army that Wendy was standing right by Army's seat.

"Wendy?" Army exclaimed as he turned to look at her.

"Hi, Army," Wendy said, smiling down at Army.

Army couldn't tell if it was sun blindness or just his attraction to her, but as Wendy smiled, Army saw an array of colorful dots swirling in the air about her.

"I said hello, Army," Wendy continued in a bit of an urgent way.

Army knew he was expected to reply, but the sparkly lights dancing around Wendy's head mesmerized him. He rubbed his eyes, took a breath, and finally responded.

"Hello, what do you want?" he said, and then immediately castigated himself for being so lame.

Wendy knelt down so that she was face-level with Army and she whispered conspiratorially to him, "Did you read my note? I know."

Army was nervously happy that he was suddenly in a whispered conversation with the girl of his dreams. "Literally of my dreams," he thought.

"Do you understand? I *know*." Wendy said, arching her eyebrows in the way people do to indicate that there are tacit layers of meaning underneath what is explicitly being said.

"You know? Know what?"

"I know about," and now Wendy leaned closer to Army and lowered her voice even more, "I know about…"

The bus came to its last stop at school, and the sudden braking motion threw Wendy off balance. Army grabbed her before she could fall to the floor. She looked up at Army and said with wonder, "You saved me."

"I just steadied you so you wouldn't fall."

"No, Army, you have to save me!"

With the bus now stopped, the kids were exiting and the ones behind Wendy started shouting.

"Come on, get out of the way!" yelled a girl named Louisa.

"Let's go!" shouted Francine, who was Mr Dupont's daughter.

"Oh look, it's Wendy and Army!" snarked Thomas, the new student who had arrived from Germany last year.

Army let go of Wendy and she ran to the exit. Save her? Why does she keep saying that? Does she know about Langdimania? No, that can't be, she couldn't be frozen there, and here with him at the same time. But what else could she mean? Wait a moment, of course! She means the school musical!

"She wants me to try out for the Scarecrow!" Army cried aloud.

"Who wants you to do what?" Willie responded.

But before Army could explain, he was interrupted by his exiting classmates.

"Move it, Army!" Louisa ordered.

"Yeah, Army, your love is getting away!" Thomas teased.

Army blushed and quickly exited the bus with his schoolmates close behind. They continued taunting him as they walked up the sidewalk path to the school.

"Hey Army, looks like Wendy doesn't want to be drafted!" Thomas baited.

Army put his hand in his pocket as he hurried along and began pressing the buttons of The Langdim Finder. He concentrated on each kid following him. Louisa, who didn't have to take a language class because she already spoke Spanish in her family, Francine the French teacher's daughter, and Thomas from Berlin. They were now teasing him by using actual army recruitment slogans against him. Instead of the official mottos of "Be all you can be", "Army strong" and "Army of One" they began bullying Army with chants of "Be as small as you can be", "Army's wrong", and "Army of One", which still worked as a taunt without even having to change anything!

Army was now sweating and red in the face as he turned on his antagonists and let loose a verbal torrent in a mix of Spanish, French, and German.

"Todos ustedes son un montón de idiotas! Vous ne savez rien! Ich bin der König von Langdimania und sie… sie… sind dumme Köpfe!" ("You are all a bunch of idiots! You know nothing! I am the king of Langdimania and you… you… are stupid heads!")

The kids stopped in their tracks with their mouths hung open in shock.

"Sí, lo sé. Ich bin fantastisch. S'y habituer!" ("Yeah, I know. I'm awesome. Get used to it!") Army concluded.

He then turned victoriously on his heel and marched away into the school, happy that his newfound abilities seemed to constantly allow him such triumphant exits.

Once they had passed through the school's entrance, Army and Willie headed towards their home room, unaware that a determined Mrs Czernowski was surreptitiously following them. She needed to get something on Army and had been spending her breaks between classes stalking him, though she could never get close enough to glean any information she could use. But today she was trying out a new plan and had dressed in a janitor's uniform with her hair tucked back under a hat and wearing sunglasses. She had even taken Mr Finch's advice and showered before arriving to school, so that her - as Mr Finch had so diplomatically put it - "delightful aroma", wouldn't give her away.

Her plan had worked. Army and his friend had passed right by her while she pretended to be mopping the hallway floor, and she continued on behind them, well within hearing distance.

Willie was speaking, "So, Army, what were you talking about on the bus? Something about the musical?"

Mrs Czernowski's heart began to race. The musical? Is Army interested in auditioning after all?

"It's Wendy. She's trying out for Dorothy in the school play and she wants me to audition for the Scarecrow so that I can save her from the Wicked Witch of the West! I'm going to do it!"

"But I thought you said you hated the musicals and that Mrs Czernowski hates you?" Willie rejoined, while the busload of kids tried to push past them.

"I do, and she does, but I've got a card up my sleeve!"

Suddenly, the morning bell rang and the boys raced along with the rest of the kids to their homerooms to register for the day.

Left behind in their wake, Mrs Czernowski shook with delight as a grin slithered its way across her face like a gecko pouncing on a fly.

"The school musical? It's perfect, so deliciously perfect!" Mrs Czernowski cackled, and her ghoulish laughter ricocheted down the now empty hallway.

CHAPTER 36

Vladimir was the first to rise. Lucy and Josiah had stayed the night. None of them had wanted to part and be alone after such a momentous evening. The fire had burnt out long ago and the tower had turned cold as the first rays of the morning sun shone into the room. Vladimir had just had the strangest dream and he was pondering it as he went about cleaning out the ashes and burnt remainders of the previous night's story-fire. He had dreamt that he was in a library, which wasn't strange in and of itself as the pig's home was almost a library anyway. No, it was that he had wings and he was floating along rows of books. He was trying to read the titles on the bindings of the tomes, but the letters were all mixed up, as they usually are in dreams. And then, looking down, he saw the youngster named Army. The boy was walking down the aisles of the library when Vladimir chuckled aloud, "Did you ever notice that aisle and isle sound the same?"

The boy looked around to see where the voice had come from, but he didn't look up and see Vladimir.

"It's Army, the boy that needs to rescue the girl," Vladimir thought to himself in his dream. He wanted to get the boy to come to Langdimania, but he couldn't figure out how. If only he could get a map to the boy that would direct him back to the tower. A map! That was it. Suddenly, the dream shifted, and Vladimir was standing at his Patternology table in the tower looking through the various items on his desk until he came across an old atlas of Langdimania. He diligently tore out a map, folded it up, and placed it carefully into an envelope. The dream switched again, and Vladimir was back in the library, floating over Army as if he had never left.

The pig thought, "Now I'll place the envelope in the book nearest Army…"

He did so, and then he concentrated with all of his might, "Army, pick up the book!" He thought it over and over, imagining that his thoughts were a beam of light directed at Army's mind, and it worked! Army reached up and took down the book that Vladimir had placed the map into.

"At last!" Vladimir smiled in triumph. And with that thought, he had awoken.

Lucy's yawning interrupted Vladimir's remembrances of his dream. "You're up," she said to Vladimir, and then looking over at Josiah asleep on his perch with his head tucked under a wing, she remarked, "How does he do that?"

"Do what?" Vladimir enquired back at her.

"Sleep like that."

"What's so unusual about that? I've seen you sleep standing up."

"Yes, but with all four hooves on the ground like a sensible animal, not balancing on a perch!"

Josiah must have sensed he was the topic of conversation, for he too was now awake. Lifting his head and shaking out his feathers, Josiah said, "Good morning everybody. Has the Army arrived yet for morning tea?"

Lucy laughed at Josiah, but Vladimir was once again looking off into the distance, as he so often did, lost in thought.

"What is it, Vladimir?" Lucy chided.

"Hmm? Oh nothing, Lucy," he said. "It's just that I had a very odd dream last night."

"Are there dreams that aren't odd?" Josiah asked. "I mean, dreams are always weird, aren't they? Maybe if you had a dream that was just like a perfectly ordinary day where you dream that you wake up, you fly down to the river to hunt water-striders, and then you return to your nest for a nap; a dream like that where the clouds don't turn into flowers and the bulls don't live in your tree, where you just eat and fly and nap; now a dream like that would be weird."

"I dreamt that I gave Army a map so that he could return to Langdimania and save The Girl," Vladimir said flatly.

"Oh, yeah, OK," Josiah agreed, "that's odd."

CHAPTER 37

A rmy had an entire half of a school day to get through before the afternoon try-outs for the musical. This would be a piece of cake. He had already used blackmail to get out of French, why not use it to get into the musical? Sure, it was "the wrong thing to do", but is it evil to use evil to defeat evil? Army wasn't sure of that, but if it resulted in him getting to be with Wendy, such moral dilemmas could wait until he was older. Ah, the freedom of youth!

When Army arrived at the auditorium for his audition, he saw that the place was overflowing with eager students. Willie was on stage belting out an off-key rendition of 'If I Only Had A Heart' and there was Wendy coming up the aisle towards Army.

"Hi Army, are you auditioning?" she asked.

Army was confused; hadn't she asked him too? Wasn't he, the Scarecrow, supposed to save her, Dorothy?

"Um, yeah," he muttered.

"That's cool," she said, and then, lowering her voice, she continued, "and remember, you have to rescue me."

"Yeah, I know, I read the script," Army replied, proud that he finally understood what was going on.

"The script?" Wendy said, "What script?"

"The Wizard of Oz, of course."

"What are you talking about?"

"What are *you* talking about?"

"Abraham Armstrong Allen, you're up!" came the bellowing voice of Mrs Czernowski.

"I've got to go," Army said to Wendy.

"But," Wendy began, before she was interrupted by another shout from the chorus teacher.

"Let's go, Abraham, we haven't got all day!"

"Don't worry, Wendy, I've got this. I'll get the part of the Scarecrow and I'll rescue you from the Wicked Witch." Army said gallantly, so pleased that he was finally going to make up for messing up big time with the scroll.

"No, you idiot," Wendy cried out, "not in the musical, in Langdimania. The animal's story says so. You have to do it or I'll be stuck in The Well forever!"

"What? Langdimania? Talking animals? How do you know about that?

"NOW, Mr Allen!" Mrs Czernowski thundered.

"Go," Wendy said.

"But I have to talk with you," Army protested.

"Meet me at my locker during lunchtime and we'll figure this out."

"But…"

"ARMY!"

"Go," Wendy repeated, as she turned and headed for the exit.

Bewildered, Army headed down the aisle to where Mrs Czernowski was fuming.

"And what song are you going to torture us with today, Abraham?"

Abraham? She had agreed to calling him Army. Had she forgotten their deal?

"Excuse me, Mrs Czernowski, but could I speak with you privately for a moment?"

Obviously, she needed to be reminded of who was in charge in this relationship.

"Why certainly, young man," she replied, way more enthusiastically than the situation called for, or so it seemed to Army.

She ushered Army backstage and then continued, "Well?"

Still knocked off center by Wendy's revelation, Army stammered his threat, "Listen, Mrs Czernowski, we have a deal. You call me Army now, you see?"

"Oh, is that so?" she retorted.

"Yeah, and what's more, there's no need for me to audition. We both know you have to give me any part I want, and I want to be The Scarecrow."

"Well, that'd be perfect for a boy with no brains."

"What?" Army cried, aghast at this rapidly devolving situation.

"Now you listen to me, Abraham. The deal's off. I know how badly you want that part, but you won't get it unless you turn over that recording."

"Hey, you can't blackmail the blackmailer!"

"I think I just did." Mrs Czernowski gleamed in triumph.

The world began to swim in front of Army's eyes. If he gave her the tape, then Mr Finch could easily reinstate Army into the French class he dreaded where, by now, he knew Mr Dumont was just itching to fail him. He'd be left back a year and Wendy would move up a grade ahead of him! But if he didn't give up the tape, he wouldn't get the part and be able to save Wendy.

"Save Wendy?" he suddenly thought to himself. "Wait a second, she just said she doesn't need saving in the musical; she said she needs rescuing in Langdimania!"

Army suddenly felt his indecision fade away. He turned on Mrs Czernowski and said in a scary, even monotone, "You will never get the tape. Our original deal is back on," and then he shouted so everyone could hear, "and I don't care about your stupid musical or your sadistic auditions. I could write and direct a better musical myself!"

And with that he stalked out of the theatre, leaving behind a dazed and defeated Mrs Czernowski.

CHAPTER 38

It was torture waiting for the lunchtime bell. Army had to talk to Wendy before he could even think of trying a return to Langdimania. Had she been there too? What was she so scared of? Was it the panther? The questions swirled around Army's head like autumn leaves caught in the wind. It was all so hard to piece together. If Wendy had really been to Langdimania, then it was real and he wasn't having mini-comas, it wasn't all some sort of brain spasm. But maybe his speaking in other languages and the episodes of visiting the other dimension were unrelated to each other. He hadn't thought of that. Maybe it was just a coincidence, and the map from the book in the library, and Wendy asking for Army to save her just before the musical auditions, were all just an elaborate ruse to get back at him for the royal chain letter.

He could imagine Cathy egging Wendy on to do it, and they were always conspiring together. But that was crazy, wasn't it? Well, not any crazier than thinking that he and Wendy were visiting another dimension but just hadn't run into each other over there yet. It was all too much, there were so many variables, he just had to talk to Wendy and find out the truth once and for all.

Finally, the bell rang and the hallways filled with kids rushing to their lockers for their jackets, skateboards, and back packs. Army joined the flow of hurrying students, making his way to the annex where Wendy had her locker. He was very nervous, not only because he might finally get some answers, but because he still adored the girl and found it almost impossible to talk to her. What if it really was a trick and he was now walking straight into it?

"Hey, Army!" a voice behind him shouted. Army turned around to see Mike standing there. "You want to have lunch on the bleachers?"

"Oh, hi, Mike," Army said, realizing he hadn't spoken to his friend since 'The Cookie Incident'. "I want to but I've something else I have to do."

"Yeah, yeah," Mike said disappointedly, "seems you always have something else to do." He turned around and walked away, saying desolately over his shoulder, "Later."

"No, wait, Mike!" Army yelled after him, but Mike was gone, swallowed into the river current of exiting happy kids.

Army sighed a lonesome sigh, realizing he hadn't been the best friend one could be lately, and this made him even more determined to see Wendy and get things straightened out once and for all.

CHAPTER 39

The panther stood on top of a small hill near the start of the isthmus that connected F'orest to F'arm. He had been standing post there alert for a long while. His head was lifted and his nose held high, sniffing the air as the breezes blew by. He had lost the power of language, but he hadn't lost the scent of the boy. There was the slightest trace of it coming from the direction of F'arm, so slight that the big cat knew it wasn't recent. But he was patient. He could wait until a stronger image, a current impression, made its way to him again, and then the hunt would begin.

CHAPTER 40

Wendy opened her locker to get her lunch. Her mind was a million miles away. She'd been in a fuddle all day trying to figure out how Army was connected to the gemstone, The Wishing Well, and the talking animals. She needed to know why these animals felt he could save her. She didn't want to dream about being trapped floating in a well for the rest of her life. It would drive her mad! Why are dreams always so frustrating? Why couldn't Army be the one who was stuck, and she could save him? She grabbed her lunch from the locker's top shelf and slammed the door in frustration only to find Army standing there smiling sheepishly at her.

"Army!"

"Hi, Wendy, do you have a minute to talk?"

"Enough with all of his shy ways," Wendy thought. It was cute, but now was not the time for cuteness. Now was the time to cut to the chase and figure out what was going on.

"Of course I have time to talk, Army," she said. "First of all, how much do you know about my dreams of my Langdimania? How did you find out? Did you sneak into my house and read my diary for goodness sake?"

"What?" Army replied incredulously. "Are you nuts? *Your* Langdimania? Langdimania is *my* idea. Why are you playing this trick on me? My life is weird enough without you driving me crazy too!"

"Look Army, your life isn't driving you crazy. You're already crazy!"

They were both shouting at each other until Wendy noticed that the other kids in the hall were now staring at them. So, she turned her anger at them too, "And all of you nosy bodies can close your gaping mouths and get lives!"

She then grabbed Army by his elbow and said, "Come with me." She marched him into the empty history classroom at the end of the row of lockers.

Once inside, once the door closed behind them, Army said, "Alright already, what's going on?"

"You tell me, Army. This all started when you tried to give me that stupid scroll on the bus."

"It wasn't stupid. I was giving you a kingdom!"

"It wasn't a kingdom, it was a game, a ridiculous game!"

"If the game is so ridiculous then why are you still playing it? Why did you give me that note in Mr Fulmar's class? 'Save me Army'. I thought you meant from the Wicked Witch in the play! Save you? Save you from who?"

"Not who," Wendy yelled back as tears started to well up in her eyes, "what! The Wishing Well, I'm stuck in The Wishing Well!"

And then her emotions got the best of her and she started crying. Army didn't know what to do and instinctively he looked around for a grown-up to help, as kids do. But it was just the two of them alone in the room. He took a breath, patted Wendy's shoulder, and said, "Okay, okay, calm down, it'll be okay."

Now Wendy's tears of frustration turned back into anger and she snapped, "Will it? Every night I go to sleep and I have the same dream. I'm floating in a well and I can't get out and the animals that are gathered outside of it are telling a story of how you are supposed to save me!"

"The animals talk?" Army asked.

"Yes."

"Wendy, you said this all started after you tore up the scroll. Did anything else happen that day?"

"What do you mean?"

"I don't know, something unusual, something like the lights flashing on and off before you went to sleep?"

"No, nothing like that. The only other thing was the gemstone."

"The gemstone? What gemstone?"

"It was weird," Wendy said, relieved to finally have someone to share her story with. "It almost seemed to drop up out of a puddle and into my hand. I think it may have come from The Well."

Army's face lit up with wonder and he said, "Listen, Wendy, I believe you. This is all really happening. The stone, The Well, the animals, Langdimania. I think it's all real somehow. I've been there too."

Army took The Langdim Finder out of his pocket and showed it to Wendy.

"This is The Langdim Finder. I can speak any language with it and I can travel to Langdimania as well."

"That's just a plastic toy, Army! I can't believe you'd keep on making fun of me!"

"No, no, I'm not making fun. It really can do those things. I just have to push the buttons and concentrate. I can prove it to you. We'll go together."

"Go where?"

"To Langdimania!"

"What are you talking about?"

"Trust me. I've done it before. Maybe if we hold hands while I do it, we can both make the jump."

Army extended his hand to Wendy. She hesitated, but then figured it would either work or not. Either way, she'd find out the truth. She took Army's hand and watched as he closed his eyes, concentrated hard, pushed the buttons, and chanted a single word, "F'arm."

CHAPTER 41

The animals had just finished breakfast and were trying to decide which of them would stand guard in the tower while the other two ventured out to gather food, when the lights began blinking on and off again.

"He's coming! He's coming!" cried Josiah. He jumped from his perch and began to fly around the room, got confused by the rapidly strobing lights, flew straight into a wall, and slid to the floor. Moaning, he cawed weakly, "Oh, that's going to leave a bump."

Meanwhile, Lucy shuffled back and forth unsure of where to sit, while Vladimir simply turned to face the bench that Army had last been seen sitting on. Sure enough, a few moments later, Army appeared, standing on the bench with his eyes closed tight. One arm was outstretched and in his hand he held aloft The Langdim Finder. He was rapidly pressing its buttons while intensely repeating the word 'F'arm'. His other arm extended in a downward angle with his hand held out, as if he had just been holding something dear in it. The flashing of the lights ceased and he opened his eyes.

"We did it!" Army exclaimed. "Wendy, we're here!"

He turned to Wendy only to find that she hadn't materialized with him. He looked about and saw the pig and the sheep staring up at him, and the crow limping slowly across the floor to join them.

"Hello, again," Vladimir said carefully, so as not to startle Army.

"Are you alright, dear?" Lucy mewed, trying to emulate Vladimir's practiced nonchalance.

"Maybe next time kid, you could arrive without all the crazy lights?" Josiah remarked.

"Where is she? Where's Wendy?" Army beseeched them. He felt lost without her, as if some unseen force had torn him in half leaving a gaping, empty feeling in his chest.

"She's floating in The Well," Vladimir said.

"Why don't you come down from there and join us?" Lucy smiled at him.

Army jumped down from the bench and continued shouting at them, "Floating in a well? Why don't you get her out? She could drown!"

"Drown?" Josiah laughed. "Drown in the air?"

Army was near tears. "What are you talking about? Drown in the water!"

Lucy replied this time, "But there's no water in The Well. At least, I don't think so. It goes on forever. Please try to relax."

Army felt defeated. Why hadn't Wendy made the jump with him? Nothing in this place made any sense. His knees felt weak and he allowed himself to slowly sit down on the cushioned seat.

"I don't understand," Army said.

"It's time you heard The Story," Vladimir said to Army.

"The story?" Army asked.

"Oh no, not again!" Josiah wailed. "We just stayed up all night telling it!"

Vladimir gave Josiah the "you really don't want to mess with me right now" look that only a large pig can give and said, "Josiah, why don't you and Lucy go out and gather food for our lunch and dinner while I have a chat with our guest."

"Yes, Josiah," Lucy said supportively. "Let's go and see what we can find."

The sheep and crow bade goodbye to the boy and the pig, and left the tower to go scavenging. Once they were out the door, Vladimir turned solemnly to Army and asked, "Have you ever made a fire in a fireplace before?"

CHAPTER 42

A h, there it was. Though it was as faint as the sigh of a snowflake landing on fur, it stood out brightly, for he had never smelled anything else like it before. Its intriguing notes of sweat and flesh, mixed with a trace of cotton ripening in the sun, played upon his nostrils. The human boy was back.

The panther took one more big whiff of the delicious scent and swallowed as if it were food already in his maw. He then slinked down the side of the hill and began his journey toward the source of it all, towards F'arm and the boy.

CHAPTER 43

A s he finished telling The Story to Army, Vladimir intoned, "And so it was and so it is that we continue to tell this tale to each other on the nights of the full moon at the base of The Wishing Well so as not to forget the girl who we failed and the army who will save her."

The room in the tower grew silent once again, except for the occasional crackle from the fireplace. The enormity of the moment gripped these two creatures, human and porcine, and all the myriad differences between them of time, space, and species fell away under the power of the story and the realization that they were living it.

"Wow," Army said as he passed his fingers through his hair. "That's – this – it's all just so amazing."

"Indeed," agreed Vladimir.

"So, Joseph dropped his Langdim Finder, the gemstone, into The Wishing Well and then a little later Wendy appeared in there?"

"Yes," Vladimir replied.

"Or so it seems," Army said mysteriously.

"What are you thinking?" Vladimir asked.

"Well, there are a few disruptions in the patterns."

"Disruptions? Like what?"

"Wendy, for instance. In the story, you said she always appears during the full moon. That would mean months have gone by. The story also talks about much longer stretches of time, years even, from when Joseph first found the stone and dropped it down The Well, to Wendy only first starting to dream about The Well last week!"

Army suddenly noticed that Vladimir was staring at him like he was from another world. Which, of course, he was, but he thought that they'd gotten past that by now.

"What is it? Why are you looking at me like that?"

"Because you said some words I never had in my head before and it explains a lot."

"Words? Which words?"

"Weeks, months, years. Time."

"Time? You've never heard of time?"

"Not in this linear, measured way you're describing. As if there were a space between events that could be perceived as a kind of separation."

"Well, how do you measure time, then?"

"I don't."

"How do you know when to eat?"

"When I'm hungry."

"How do you know when to meet someone else?"

"When I smell where they are."

"But times passes. In the story, time passes like from when Joseph loses the stone to when he gets it back."

"I see what you mean now, at least I think I do, but the story is one whole thing and everything in it is happening at the same time. Like a book."

"A book?"

"Yes, the contents of the book unfold in an intended order, but the book itself contains them all at the same time."

155

Army's mouth fell open. It made sense in a weird way. What he thought of as time moving along, the animals of Langdimania seemed to experience as a process that happens all at once but unfolds gradually to the one experiencing it.

The two beings sat silently for a while, each trying to grasp how the other was perceiving time, and just as each one thought they understood and started to verbalize it, the concept would fade like a dream.

"Time here is dreamlike," Army said. "When we are in each other's worlds, we are in the dream of that world and so time is fluid and dependent on the observer!"

Vladimir excitedly continued the reasoning, "So, I can be here with you and it seems like a few 'hours' have passed for you, but at The Wishing Well it might be what you call a 'month'... yes?"

Army agreed, "And in my world it might be just a few minutes!"

Vladimir then had a realization. "Dreams."

"Yeah?"

"Did you by any chance have a dream of being in a library and reading an atlas?"

Army was dumbstruck.

"I take it by your reaction that you have?" Vladimir pressed.

"No, not a dream. Real life. I was in my school library and everything got weird and... and... dreamlike!"

"I was there!"

"What?"

"I just dreamt last night of flying over you in the library and putting the map inside the book!"

"Last night? But that happened a few days ago!"

"Wow," they both said simultaneously.

Just then, the door to the tower room opened and Lucy and Josiah came bustling in, carrying the supplies for the afternoon's lunch and the evening's dinner.

"Well, you're back and it's about time," Vladimir boomed with a wink at Army.

"Yeah, it's about *time*!" Army joined in with a laugh.

"What's with you guys?" Josiah asked.

"Nothing at all, Josiah, we're just hungry," said Vladimir.

"You're always hungry," retorted Josiah.

Lucy joined in, "Well, I'll bet young Army must be hungry as well, aren't you dear?"

Army had been so involved in the tale that Vladimir had told and their subsequent discussion about the disparities in how time worked in their respective realities, that he hadn't thought about how hungry he was. He was famished.

"Why yes, miss, I mean, ma'am, or is it, um…" stammered Army.

"Lucy. Just call me Lucy. Everyone else does," Lucy said to Army, as she laid out plates for everybody.

"Miss Lucy," Army said.

"No, just Lucy is fine."

"So, what's the plan now, Vladimir?" asked Josiah.

"Quite simply, we eat," said the pig, joyfully eyeing the plates of food that Lucy was preparing.

"And then what?"

"And then the moon will be full and we'll go to The Wishing Well and see what Army here can do to save The Girl."

CHAPTER 44

A rmy's walk to The Wishing Well started out in an ordinary way, if walking down winding stone tower steps with three talking animals discussing time as if it was a new concept could be considered ordinary.

"So, what you are saying," Lucy continued, "is that time to Army is more like a single string rather than the rich tapestry we know it to be."

"Yes, Lucy, a very good analogy," Vladimir replied. "Army's kind don't seem to interpret time as one never-ending, never-beginning, everywhere at once, all around us, fluid part of life but rather as things that are behind them and things that are in front of them with themselves always in the middle."

"But if time includes these things that are in front of them but "haven't happened yet" then those things aren't really there at all," Josiah said.

Upon reaching the bottom of the steps, Vladimir engaged the door opening mechanism. As the huge, wooden door creaked open and the quartet walked out into the chill dusk air, Josiah persisted, "And if they're not really there at all then this thing, this 'future', is just a - a- well, a dream."

"Sounds fun," Lucy said, trying to soften Josiah's ramblings so the boy wouldn't feel insulted.

"Well, time flies when you're having fun!" Army said, laughing at the absurdity of it all.

"Ah, but where to?" Vladimir smiled back.

"Maybe Army's time flies here and vice versa!" cried Josiah, enjoying the debate that continued as they walked across grassy meadows towards a hill that began to rise in the distance.

Eventually, the discussion about time dwindled into the kind of silence that a long walk will engender, until Josiah had a curious thought which he shared out loud. "Say, I just thought of something, if the gemstone that Wendy found was the same one that my extremely great grandfather dropped into The Wishing Well, then where did Army get the Langdim Finder?"

Josiah's question hung in the air like the smell of a burning dinner until Army said, "It was a birthday present. I saw a basket of toys and chose it for myself," and then, after a sudden realization, he continued excitedly, "but now that I think of it, there's something that I forgot about until now."

Vladimir's eyebrows raised at this as he sensed a new pattern forming and he asked, "Forgot about what?"

"The bird. The black bird that I saw in the store. I thought I saw it drop something into the basket. That's why I looked in there to begin with! If that was Joseph, then how did the gemstone split into the one that Wendy has and also become a toy in a basket?"

Though Army's questions weren't directed at Vladimir, the gang all looked at him for the answers; figuring these kinds of things out was his job, after all.

And so, Vladimir spoke up, "We've all had things happen to us that by their very remarkability become unremarkable, simply because the secrets that the events reveal are too incongruous to our perception of the way things are. When they first occur, like thinking of a friend and then they appear, we are delighted by the magic of it but within moments that is laughed away as we try to decide where to go to lunch together. Some have theorized that these types of things happen to us all of the time but we filter them out because it would be too hard to return to what we were doing. For instance, how to explain seeing the previously thought of friend? Telepathy? Our thoughts creating reality? Mere coincidence? But isn't calling such a coincidence 'mere', simply another way to put it in a box and file it out of sight? And, even more, aren't the things all around us just as magical as a coincidental meeting? The blossoming of a flower, the direction the river flows, our being together right now? How did any of this happen? We were astounded to meet Army and vice versa, but now, here we are and it seems as natural as can be. Perhaps when Joseph dropped the stone into the well it fell through to Army's dimension where it simply found its way to where it was supposed to be. Who's to say that a stone that can endow us with language and give Army passage to our world isn't capable of such things? And is it any more wonderous than all of the amazing things around us right now that we don't question? The unending sky, the growing fields, our beating hearts? Indeed, if there's one thing my life as a Patternologist has taught me, it's that the miraculous holds us as intimately as the air we breathe; it's just a matter of noticing and believing it."

Vladimir's enlightening words both awed and reassured his friends. They resumed their hike but before long they heard a wild howl behind them. Army turned in fright, horrified that it was the panther but finding, instead, that it was a dog. A large, golden, labrador to be exact, that bounded up to them shouting, "You're him! You've arrived!"

Army laughed in delight, not only at the good-naturedness of the dog running around and grinning at him, but also in relief that it wasn't the panther.

"Easy, Beauregard, easy," Lucy said.

"You are him, aren't you?" Beauregard asked Army with big, trusting eyes.

"Well, I'm me," Army replied.

"Of course, you're him," Josiah said to Army, and then turning to the dog he added, "He's him."

Beauregard howled again.

"Why are you howling if you can talk?" Army asked.

"I'm alerting my pack, of course!" Beauregard shouted, and then he began howling some more. In the distance, Army could hear dogs howling back.

"Now we're in for it," Josiah remarked.

"It's OK, Josiah," Vladimir said, "once we left the tower, Army's scent was carried by the wind. Now everyone knows the good news, and that's just the way it should be. Let's keep walking."

Army repeated Vladimir's words to himself, "Army's scent was carried by the wind. Now everyone knows…"

CHAPTER 45

The hunt was on. The wild cat could feel the thrill of it as he ran across the great sandy strip of land that separated the two animal territories of F'orest and F'arm. With the sun just setting in the sky, it would be dark by the time he reached the border where the bulls stood sentry. He never crossed the line, as the anger of the bulls was not worth a pig or a sheep when deer and fowl were plentiful in F'orest. However, the temptation of this new prey, this boy, was too much to bear. His smell hinted at delicacies the panther had hitherto only dreamed of. Beyond that thought, there was something else; a faded memory from his first engagement with the strange animal. A taste he experienced beyond ordinary sense. A glimmer of light.

As he ran along in the dusk, the panther scented a wild hare shivering in the brush, bringing with it a salivating promise of a full belly, but the panther slowed down not a whit. His target was chosen, and nothing would stop him until he had his fangs deep in the boy's throat.

CHAPTER 46

The original band of animals from the Patternologist's tower had grown considerably in size. More and more clans joined them as they marched toward The Wishing Well, some following from behind while others ran up front to get glimpses of Army. Those close enough to the primary quartet would send news back as to what was being said. The sheep and crows that had joined the procession cawed and bleated proudly as one of their kind had become so closely involved with The Arrival. The sun had fully set by the time they all had climbed the short hill leading up to The Well and the full moon was just now peeking out from behind the evening clouds.

Army turned around to take it all in. Animals of all sorts stood, squatted, sat, and lay before him as birds flew amongst them. He saw horses, dogs, pigs, sheep, rams, and rabbits. He saw turtles, otters, rats, and mice. He saw crows, sparrows, jays, and ducks. All of them alert, hopeful, and waiting for Army to save The Floating Girl, to save Wendy.

Army's face flushed, and he started to sweat. He had been so caught up in his conversations with the animals that he'd forgotten exactly what was expected of him. But now, looking over the multitude that was gathered before him, he became acutely aware of the responsibility that had been thrust upon him. Save the girl. How?

"It's time, Army," Vladimir said solemnly to Army.

The guards at The Well this night were a horse named Gladys and a hound dog named Jack. They both stood tall and proud as Army approached them. They bowed awkwardly and then stepped back to allow Army room and to hold back the onlookers.

"OK, folks," said Jack, in a deep voice that sounded as if he occasionally gargled with gravel, "let's give The Arrival some room."

The animals stepped back, forming a half circle of space with Army at the center where he stood shifting nervously on his feet. He had his hand in his pocket and was seriously considering using The Langdim Finder to flash out of the situation, when Josiah alighted on his shoulder.

"Let it go, kid," Josiah whispered in Army's ear, "you can do this."

Army took a deep breath, stepped up to the wall of The Wishing Well and looked down. He turned back to Lucy and Vladimir and said, "She's not there."

"What?" exclaimed Vladimir and he rushed up to look for himself. The animals that had overheard Army were now communicating the news to the others behind them, and a wave of consternation flowed across the assembly. Vladimir turned to Jack and Gladys and said, "Have you seen her?"

Gladys answered, "We just started our shift after dinner. We thought she'd appear with the moon, but we haven't seen or heard her yet."

"I don't understand," Vladimir grumbled, "she should be here; the moon is full. Army is supposed to rescue her and herald in a new age for Langdimania."

Army became more alarmed when he heard Vladimir say this. Though he was worried about trying to figure out how he was supposed to save Wendy, he was still intent on succeeding. But no one had mentioned anything about heralding in some sort of new age. What was that supposed to mean?

Army looked sideways at Josiah who was still perched on his shoulder and said quietly to him, "What's Vladimir mean by my bringing in a new age?"

Josiah winked at Army and chuckled, "Ha! You didn't see that one coming, did you?"

The murmurs from the gathered animals were growing louder now as their mild unease began to turn into a more boisterous unrest.

"Josiah," Army pleaded, "what are you talking about?"

"Well, it's really quite simple," Josiah said, "after you save the girl, a new age will dawn where the animals of F'arm and the beasts of F'orest will learn to live at peace with one another. No more nighttime raids by the foxes, the owls, and the wild cats. The bulls will stand down and once again lie in the fields with the cows, and the great struggle will finally come to an end."

CHAPTER 47

Seeing how shaken Army was by what Josiah had revealed, Lucy came up beside him and said, "There's nothing to worry about, Army. Vladimir's predictions may be a bit askew from time to time but ultimately he's always been right. He foresaw your arrival and he was right. He knew we'd all be gathered here at The Wishing Well eventually and he was right. You will rescue the girl and a new age will dawn."

Army had to almost shout now to be heard above the din of the animal's cries of disappointment and concern at there being no girl to save from The Wishing Well.

"But Lucy, I have no idea how to do it. Wendy didn't make the jump with me. You all said she'd be here at The Well but she's not. How can I save someone who's not even here?"

Vladimir joined in, "Army, she'll be here. Worry not," and then he added darkly, "There is a sense to things, even when they go wrong."

"Go wrong?" Army wondered out loud.

Vladimir cursed himself for allowing his personal foreboding to alarm the child and so he quickly clarified, "I simply mean that things happen for a reason. Birds need to fly so they have wings, bulls need to protect so they have horns, pigs need to forage so we have strong snouts. You need to rescue the girl so a way will be shown."

Though he felt comforted by his new friend's explanation, Army was at a loss. The gathering was turning louder and uglier by the second. He clasped the Langdim Finder, and Josiah felt the movement from his perch on Army's shoulder.

"What are you planning to do, kid?" he asked Army.

Army felt embarrassed being caught out for his fearful behavior and he decided to confess to the crow, whispering in his ear.

"I'm scared, Josiah," he said, "The animals are so upset and if I don't do something quick they might turn on me; but I don't know what to do!"

"You can start by saying something to calm everyone down!"

"But what do I say?"

Vladimir had been lost in thought for the last few minutes but now his eyes lit up and he excitedly shouted to Army, "Army, what did you mean when you said to Lucy that Wendy didn't *make the jump with you*?"

Before Army could reply, Jack the hound dog interrupted, "Excuse me folks, but we need a plan here. Things are getting out of hand."

The quartet from the tower were now pressed up against The Well with Jack and Gladys forming a barrier along with a few more guards who had jumped in to help. Beyond them, the other animals had turned from a gathering into a mob, and they were not happy at all.

"Where's the Army that's supposed to defeat the beasts of F'orest!" some yelled.

"Where's the girl? Maybe there never was a girl!" others shouted.

Army looked about and all the animals who had seemed so peaceful and happy when they first began the journey to The Well now looked frightening and dangerous. He gripped The Langdim Finder tighter and began to press a button.

Vladimir continued on, "Army! Did you leave Wendy in your world?"

"Of course!" Army thought to himself, "Wendy's not here because we didn't make the jump together! She has to use her *own* power to get here. Maybe time hasn't moved back home and she's still in the history classroom holding my hand. We need to make the jump together; she needs her stone as well!"

And then out loud he said, "That's it, Vladimir, you smart pig you! I've got to go!"

Vladimir yelled something back but the noises from the animals were too loud to hear him now. Any second and the mob would push past the guard horses and dogs and most likely tear them apart. The new age would be one of horror, not peace!

Josiah yelled right into Army's ear, "I know what you're doing but you must say something to calm everyone down before you disappear, or all hell will break loose!"

Army knew that Josiah was right, but what could he say? His thoughts jumbled around his head like confused mice in a maze until he suddenly remembered what Lucy and Vladimir had said, that there is a sense to things. Army turned to Gladys and indicted with sign language that he wanted to get on top of her. She knelt down and Army climbed on board. When Gladys stood back up, Army was high above the mob. The crowd had gone insane, braying, bleating, wailing, and roaring their dissatisfaction. Even the wind had picked up and was crying overhead. The animals, like the squirrels and rats, that could throw things were, indeed, throwing things! Pinecones, small rocks, and tufts of grass were flying through the air. Army had to duck as a stone whizzed by his head.

"Josiah!" Army shouted. "Can you summon the crows?"

"What for?"

"I need them to make a wall in the sky like in the story you told me. I need them to silence the crowd!"

"Of course!" Josiah yelled back. He took off and flew high in the air, gathering his fellow crows as he did so. Up above the land animals, and dodging the other birds in the air, Josiah's murder formed a black cloud that blotted out the full moon. Then, at Josiah's signal, they all let out a giant caw all at once that rattled like a foghorn above the jeering hordes below.

All of the animals immediately stopped what they were doing and looked up to the sky in fear and wonder. The land fell eerily silent.

"Well," thought Army, "that certainly shut them up. Good for Josiah!"

"Now, that's better!" Josiah announced to the gathering as he alighted once again onto Army's shoulder. "The human boy *is* the army. Even his name is Army! He's the one that Vladimir predicted would save The Girl and usher in the new age. But obviously, he can't save a girl that isn't there, so he's going to go back to his world and bring her here to fulfill the prophecy."

After Josiah's bold announcement, all animal eyes turned from the crows in the sky to Army sitting on top of Gladys.

"Uh, oh," Gladys muttered aloud.

Army blushed; it was now or never. He had no idea what he was going to say, he just knew he had to say something to calm the animals before he vanished. He wished he didn't have to, but he believed that he must. Wait! That was it! He knew now what he must do. He sat straight up and addressed the hundreds of animals vastly arrayed before him under the starlit sky.

"Animals!" he started, and then, realizing how silly that sounded, he quickly corrected himself and said, "Friends! What Josiah said is true. My name is Army and I've come here to rescue Wendy, The Floating Girl." He hadn't completely thought through what he was going to say. He panicked for a moment and looked over at Lucy and Vladimir for help, and that's when he remembered the wise words that the pig had said to him and he simply repeated them as best as he could remember, "There is a sense to things. Birds fly, bulls protect, and pigs smell! Um, I mean, they have strong snouts and I need to rescue the girl and so I will!"

"But how will you rescue her if she's not there?" a young sparrow named Lily cried out.

"I just will," Army replied, a bit weakly.

"But how?" the sparrow persisted, and some of the other sparrows around her took up the cry repeating, "How? It's impossible! It would take a miracle! Come to your senses!"

"Army!" someone else shouted in a familiar voice. "Wake up!"

170

Army looked around to see whose voice he had recognized, but couldn't make any kind of determination in the dark, mob-filled night. He decided it was now or never. It was time to try his trick and hope that it would work. He began furiously pressing the buttons on The Langdim Finder with one hand while he extended his other hand and pictured Wendy holding it. The stars and moon began to vibrate and Army shouted, "After all I've been through over the last few weeks, if nothing else, there is one thing I do know for certain. If someone tells you that something is impossible, that it would take a miracle, then you should rejoice, because miracles happen every day! But you must believe in them, not just wish for them, and I'll prove it! Watch closely as I'm off to find Wendy!" And, as Army said her name, he closed his eyes and pressed the buttons harder and faster than ever while concentrating on Wendy and the feel of her hand in his.

The vibrating heavens now began to flicker on and off more and more rapidly above the terrified animals until all at once everything was back to normal, except for one significant difference. Army had vanished before their eyes.

CHAPTER 48

He lost the scent again! Where did it go? Down a hole? It didn't seem like a burrowing creature, didn't smell like one, and didn't have the prerequisite claws for digging dirt. Bewildered, the panther lay flat in the tall grasses that edged the border between F'orest and F'arm. He could no longer sense the boy, but the presence of the bulls was almost overpowering. However, the great cat's sense of smell and hearing was so acute that he was able to discern two things other than the close proximity of the bulls. The first, yes, the boy had vanished, and secondly, there was a gathering of F'arm animals larger than he had ever detected before.

This situation called for patience and stealth. The panther, like all expert hunters, had both. Pressing his body as even to the ground as possible, he began his wait for the boy's return. He perked up his ears and opened his mouth to allow it to work in conjunction with his nose, so that he could peruse the various scents that the wind brought his way.

CHAPTER 49

Wendy opened her eyes and looked at Army. He had stopped his strange chanting of the word 'F'arm' and was now simply standing there with his eyes closed and his head drooping so that his chin was resting on his chest, like she'd seen him do once or twice in school. Basically, he seemed to be sleeping standing up.

"Army!" Wendy shouted at him. "Wake up!"

Army slowly opened his eyes and looked dazed, like he was coming out of a deep sleep, even though only a few seconds had gone by. He looked down at his hand holding Wendy's and then back up at her.

"Wendy! You're here!" he cried out.

"Of course I'm here you idiot! Where else would I be? What's wrong with you?"

"I was in Langdimania again. You didn't make the jump. I met with Vladimir and Lucy and Josiah and we gathered the animals on a long march to The Wishing Well, but you weren't there because you were here!"

"What are you talking about? You never left."

"What?"

"Army, you fell asleep for like a minute and now you just woke up," Wendy said, as she unclasped Army's hand.

"Fell asleep? A minute? No, I went to Langdimania. I was there for hours. I gave a speech!"

Wendy looked at Army and she knew that she had to go. She had to sort her thoughts out. Obviously, there were no such things as alternate dimensions filled with talking animals. She was the victim of a temporary hysteria caused by her wanting to believe Army, to believe *in* him. But things had gone too far.

"Army, I'm going now," she said sternly, as she gathered up her things and headed to the door.

"Wait, Wendy! The animals are waiting for us at The Well. I'm supposed to save you!"

"You need to save yourself, Army. You're sick. You're delusional and it's contagious. You had me almost believing it but they're just dreams, they're not real. Good-bye, Army."

Wendy left Army standing helplessly alone in the classroom, his heart still beating fast from the chaos he had just escaped from and the rejection he was now encompassed by.

CHAPTER 50

Army's sudden disappearance sent an electrifying shock through the gathered animals. Those closest to him when he vanished simply fell over each other in shock. Gladys, aware of the loss of her rider, looked desperately to either side of herself and then underneath. Finally, she whirled about in place looking for the boy who moments ago had been giving an inspiring rallying cry from her back. Meanwhile, Josiah frantically flapped about to avoid crashing to the ground as Army's supportive shoulder evaporated with the rest of him.

"That's it then!" Vladimir shouted to Lucy. "He's gone home to find the girl. Let's hope it works!"

"How long will it take?" Lucy shouted back over the noisy consternation of the astounded animals.

"As long as it takes!" Vladimir replied, with the usual axiom expected of a chief Patternologist, and then, turning to face the rest of the crowd, he began yelling for everyone to quiet down. Eventually, like a ripple on a lake, the animals calmed and faced Vladimir to hear what he wanted to say.

Vladimir waited dramatically for everyone to settle and then he pronounced, "The Army arrived as promised!"

There was a cheer from the crowd that settled into a miasma of whispers and trepidation.

"Yeah," heckled an otter, "but where did The Army go? And where is The Floating Girl?"

Vladimir gave the otter a disapproving look so that no one else would get the urge to interrupt him, and then he continued on, "As I said, and as I had predicted, Army was here and though he's gone, mark my words, he'll return and he will rescue the girl and usher in the New Age! Didn't his appearance as foretold, and his miraculous departure into the air, make it apparent?"

The animals cheered Vladimir's confident enthusiasm. Seemingly mollified, many of them began to sit or lie down in the grass to await Army's return. The guards of The Wishing Well once again took up their posts, and the mood on the field acquired the atmosphere of a great outdoor concert when you are a few hours early but willing to wait to hear your favorite band perform. The full moon showed overhead, and far away, along the horizon, the first gradient changes of the sky flowing from the black of night to the blue of day were beginning. Despite his bravado, Vladimir turned somberly towards the east to look for the returning sun and caught a not entirely unexpected gossamer scent of trouble coming from that direction. A distant, subtle, but unmistakably feral smell, whispering to him from F'orest.

CHAPTER 51

The rest of the school day stumbled along miserably for both Wendy and Army. They passed each other once in the hallway during the changeover in classes from history to math, but neither said a word to the other. During last period English class, Army could feel the hot glares coming at him from Wendy and Cathy across the room. This was worse than before when he thought they were conspiring about the school musical; the vibrations they gave off now were blatantly hostile. He was too scared of transporting back to Langdimania without having Wendy to rescue, that he didn't dare use his usual trick of daydreaming to make the clock on the classroom wall move quicker, in case he accidentally made the jump.

Army was at a loss. He still believed in Langdimania, even if Wendy didn't. What was she going to do about her recurring nightmare of being stuck in The Well anyway? Go to a psychiatrist? Tell her parents? Oh no! Surely, if she did either of those things, Army's name would eventually have to come up and, on top of everything else, he'd be blamed for his schoolmate's descent into insanity!

"We have to jump together again, only this time with Wendy holding onto her dream-stone while I hold The Langdim Finder," Army declared to himself. He had to convince Wendy to give it a try and right away before she found herself stuck in The Well again.

Finally, the school bell rang and the students rushed for the exit as Mr Fulmar shouted over their heads, "Don't forget to do the reading! Oh, Army, can I speak with you please?"

"Why does he keep bugging me? I need to talk to Wendy!" Army thought to himself as he hurried over and said impatiently to his teacher, "Yes?"

"Army, if you need help with the musical just let me know."

"What?"

"The play. I heard you're going to write your own musical in a sort of protest against Mrs Czernowski's, shall we say, rather unique perspective on the dramatic arts?"

"Um, Mr Fulmar," Army said, as he backed out of the room, "I'm not writing a musical."

"A musical, a play, whatever it is, let me know if you need my help."

"OK, sure thing," Army said, bewildered by a feeling that this had all happened before. "I'll let you know. I've got to run or I'll miss the bus."

Army scooped up his books and joined the exodus of kids, getting to the door just as Wendy and Cathy also did. It was now or never.

"Wendy," Army said, "I need to talk with you."

But before Wendy could reply, Cathy inserted herself between them and pronounced, "She's done talking to you, Army."

"I wasn't talking to *you*, Cathy."

"Yeah, well, I'm talking to *you*, Army, and I'm telling you that Wendy is done with your nonsense. Kings and queens of imaginary lands, turning people into servants, talking pigs, and crows!"

Army had suspected that Wendy had shared the secrets of the other dimension with her best friend, but the harshness of it being thrown back at him made him feel betrayed, and his mouth hung open with no comeback.

"Yeah, that's right Army. Wendy told me all about it and how it's given her nightmares. You should be ashamed of yourself and I've got a good mind to march over to Mr Finch's office right now and tell on you!"

"No, please Cathy, that's not a 'good mind' thing to do. That's a bad mind, a very bad mind!" Army pleaded.

They had been swept along with the rest of the children to the buses outside, where Wendy was already boarding, as Cathy continued, "Then stay away from her or I *will* tell, Army. I swear I will!"

Cathy then ran along to get her seat next to Wendy, while Army got on board and sat in the front with Willie, as usual.

"Hey Army," Willie said as Army sat down, "another boring day in school, eh?"

CHAPTER 52

Time had passed in Langdimania as time does, and eventually, the animals of F'arm had slowly left their posts by The Wishing Well and had returned to their nests, warrens, holes, and burrows. They had gone home. Once there, they continued to tell the story of The Arrival with its newly added chapters leading up to Army's disappearance and Vladimir's prediction of his return, but it was a story told with a sad mix of hope and disappointment. They wanted to have faith in the Patternologist's words but, as life moved on, it was getting harder and harder to do so, especially as rumors of attacks from F'orest were becoming more commonplace.

It started slowly at first. A rabbit gone missing here, a mouse gone missing there. Perhaps they had simply wandered off and met with ill fortune but the crows suspected the owls, the rodents suspected the foxes, and no one was certain. The spore left behind was deeper and darker than they had experienced before, and a gloom was falling over F'arm. The bulls doubled their guard, but they swore they had seen no one cross the border. They had encountered no beasts from F'orest.

It was, of course, the work of the panther. Dark as night and fast as the wind, he was able to slink past the border guards with his claws retracted to muffle his footfalls. He would cleverly roll in mud, as well, to mask his scent. He was virtually invisible as he silently invaded for his meals, while continuing to wait for the return of the boy.

The guards of The Wishing Well continued their shifts, unwatched now by the expectant eyes of their friends. Only Vladimir remained to sit vigil with them, occasionally accompanied by Lucy, Josiah, or both. One night, under a three-quarter moon, the three of them sat silently looking out over the now empty fields. Occasionally, Josiah would flutter up to the lip of The Well and look down, only to see the long black tunnel to nowhere peering back up at him.

"It's futile, Josiah," Vladimir called after him, "she only appears during a full moon."

"So far," Josiah replied, hopping back down to the grass, "so far."

They sat silently again. Lucy began wondering about the moon. Why was it always full when the girl appeared? What was the connection?

"These questions are for a Patternologist to answer," she thought to herself, and looked over at Vladimir. She had never seen him so glum before and thought better than to disturb him with her thoughts. However, Josiah had no such restraint and he had been wondering the same thing himself.

"Vladimir," Josiah began, "about the moon…"

Before he could finish, Josiah was suddenly interrupted by Jack, who was roused from his guard duty. The dog leaped to alertness with his ears pricked up, his tail straight out behind him, and peered off into the distance in the direction of the isthmus and the land of F'orest beyond.

"What is it, Jack?" Gladys asked, turning toward the east where Jack was looking. "Did you sense something?"

Jack didn't reply. He was too busy concentrating on the scent he had picked up; a scent he had been feeling in his nostrils with greater and greater frequency after the animals had left the field and the rumors of the missing had begun.

The other animals also stood now, sniffing the wind.

"It's back," Vladimir grunted.

Jack turned his head towards Vladimir and nodded.

"That murky flavor?" Lucy asked. "I smell it too."

"Yes," Gladys joined in, "like the end of summer, like dirt under hooves, like…"

"Death," Vladimir concluded, looking remorsefully at Lucy.

"I don't smell it," Josiah said, hopping up and down. "I'm going to see for myself." And off he flew in the direction his friends were all looking. The determined bird soared with all speed toward the border where the bulls stood watch. As he rocketed along, he scanned the ground below him for the mysterious creature suspected of hunting the citizens of F'arm. But a crow's sight, keen as it is, is not made for a nocturnal search like an owl's, and below him all he could make out were the shifting hues of grey and black where the ground changed levels from low hills to shallow valleys. However, as he went along, the shades became seemingly brighter, the greys lighter, the blacks now more like dark grey. By the time the herd of bulls came into view, Josiah could almost make out his shadow gliding along beneath him.

Josiah drew closer to the ground and changed his wings' angle so that he slowed and quietly landed. He looked up towards the light source and there it was, a bright, full moon illuminating the sky.

182

"Dream time," Josiah said to himself, recalling the discussions Army and Vladimir had over this whole "time" thing.

The crow's ruminations were suddenly and terribly interrupted by a huge black shadow leaping at him from out of the grass.

CHAPTER 53

B y this time, like it or not, Wendy and Army's lives were intertwined, and, after they both arrived at their respective homes, they spent the next few hours in almost the identically same way. Quick hellos and summations of their day at school to their parents (obviously leaving out all references to Langdimania, gemstones and Langdim Finders, and, of course, each other), using "doing homework" as their excuses to run up to their bedrooms to search the internet for information about lucid dreams, magic stones, and alternative dimensions (and in Wendy's case "going crazy"), coming back downstairs for dinner, and then right back upstairs to sit in front of their computers and conduct more research. Strangely enough, both of their sets of parents reacted in similar fashions as well, welcoming them home from school, putting up with their non-answer answers at dinner, and yelling up to their bedrooms that it was time to "Go to sleep now, lights out!"

In their own respective beds, Wendy and Army lay looking at their ceilings, both feeling uneasy about closing their eyes. Army was apprehensive about Wendy going back to The Well without him there to rescue her, and of the chance that she could get lost in the time stream of the dream. If they didn't jump simultaneously, he could arrive too late to save her! For her part, Wendy was worried about dreaming of being trapped in The Well again. Would it ever stop? She had taken the precaution of putting her special stone in a box in her closet to help prevent the dream from happening. Perhaps, without it in her hand, she wouldn't have the dream. She drew comfort from this thought until she had another thought that challenged it. What if she really *was* going to another world instead of just dreaming? What if she didn't have the stone with her; would she be able to return?

Wendy got out of bed and went to her closet. She took down the box, took out the stone, and got back into bed with it in her hand. She figured it was better to believe that the stone would help her back from the dream and have it with her, than to chance dreaming without the stone and be stuck in The Wishing Well and the dream forever.

Army got out of bed as well, but he had no need to retrieve his Langdim Finder from a hidden place. He always had it with him these days. Instead, he got out of his pajamas and back into his day clothes. He opened his window and climbed out onto the roof of the porch outside, where he then shimmied down the support post to the ground.

Army had a plan.

CHAPTER 54

With eyes on either side of his head, Josiah's binocular vision saved him from the panther's leaping attack. Before the big cat could land, the startled crow had taken to the air in a fury, losing only a few tail feathers to the rush of wind from the giant, swinging, feline paws. Josiah let out a shrieking caw of alarm and circled the panther from the out-of-reach safety of the air. In the distance, a few of the bulls looked towards the faraway commotion but, not having the keen hearing of dogs or the sight of crows, they went back to grazing and quietly discussing the merits of eating dry grass over wet.

"He's over here! The murdering monster is over here!" Josiah screamed towards the now completely negligent bulls to no effect. Cursing them under his breath and making a mental note that perhaps bulls alone were not the best choice for border guards, Josiah turned his attention back to the panther only to find that it had once again vanished into the blackness of the night.

Thinking that perhaps he should speed to the bulls and alert them that the panther had gotten past their guard, Josiah quickly surmised that it'd be useless. The monster was already unleashed and the bulls would never catch him in time. Josiah's thoughts quickly moved on to his comrades at The Wishing Well and of the danger they were now in. Circling in the sky, the black bird picked up speed and headed back as fast as he could to warn his friends of the murderer in their midst.

CHAPTER 55

Wendy lived a little over a half of a mile from Army's house. After sneaking down his driveway and turning right towards Wendy's home, Army thought to himself that he might be able to use The Langdim Finder to hop to Langdimania and then from there hop again to Wendy's household. However, the number of things that could go wrong were too numerous to consider, not the least of which being the weird way time flowed between the dimensions. He might end up at Wendy's a minute or a week later for all he knew. Also, and more importantly, his body seemed to stay on earth in a state of sleep while he was in Langdimania. He had no way of knowing if he could come back anywhere other than where he had jumped from. Eschewing the thought of using the finder as a travel shortcut, Army broke into a jog. He was determined to put his plan to work.

Before getting into bed, Wendy was afraid that her apprehension of having the dream about The Wishing Well again would keep her up all night. She even worried if she'd ever fall asleep again! However, once she was settled back under the covers with the gemstone in her hand, she realized how exhausted from the day's excitement she actually was, and her eyes slowly shut and her breathing slowed into the rhythm of rest.

Outside Wendy's window, Army had climbed an oak tree, from whose branches he could see inside her room. He had hoped to try to get her attention and convince her to try the jump with him again, but she had turned out her light and could possibly be asleep already.

"How can she sleep at a time like this?" Army thought to himself, and he wondered if Wendy was dreaming yet and if she had already entered The Well.

"I could throw something at the window and try to wake her up but, knowing her, she'd just yell at me again or maybe call the police," Army thought to himself, "and if I try to do the jump from here, even if I did arrive in Langdimania at the right time, my body would go limp and I'd fall out of this tree. I could climb down and hide and make the jump, but there's still no telling when I'd arrive."

It was very frustrating. It all depended on the timing of the jump and he had no way to judge that.

"Wait a second, the REM state!" Army answered his own dilemma by remembering something from his research on dreams. "Rapid Eye Movement! When someone is dreaming, their eyes move back and forth under their lids, almost as if they were watching the dream unfold. If I could get into Wendy's room, I could watch for her eyes to start moving beneath her lids and time my jump to coincide!"

It was a bold thought. Breaking into Wendy's room was wrong on so many levels but, weighed against her going crazy from the repeated dream, against the promises he had made to the animals of F'arm, and with Cathy probably planning on reporting him to the school authorities anyway, it seemed to Army to be the only option left to him.

Wendy's house was similar to Army's, and so all Army had to do was to shimmy up the porch's support to its roof and hope that Wendy's window was unlocked.

It was.

"I can't believe I'm doing this," Army whispered to himself, as he stealthily climbed over the sill and found himself standing in the dark in Wendy's room. For a second, he started to turn around and leave, but the hopeful faces of Vladimir, Lucy, Josiah, and all of the other animals flooded his mind. Army thought of their hopes for what they called a 'New Age'. He thought of Wendy's anguished face as she fretted about being stuck in The Well forever, and then he turned back around and silently stepped over to Wendy's side.

Army looked down at Wendy and saw by her steady breathing that she was definitely asleep, but it was too dark in the room to tell if she had started dreaming yet. Army's eyes were playing tricks on him in the dim light and, having never had to check for REM before, he wasn't sure what it would look like. He considered turning on the bedside lamp but he was too afraid it would wake up the girl. Anxiety at his predicament kicked in and Army unconsciously began playing with The Langdim Finder tucked away in its usual spot in his sweatshirt pocket as he searched his mind for ways to illuminate Wendy's face without waking her. Suddenly, the lighting changed.

"Oh no!" thought Army in alarm. "I've accidentally triggered my jump too soon!"

However, the strobing effect hadn't initiated. It was simply a change in lighting as if a beam had been switched on behind Army causing his shadow to fall across Wendy's silent form. He whirled around towards the window he had entered through, expecting to see a policeman holding a flashlight on him. A life in prison whipped across his petrified mind. But no one was there. It was simply the moon, coming out from behind a bank of clouds and shining its lunar light over Wendy's face.

With much relief, Army walked around to the other side of the bed so as not to block the light, thinking to himself as he did so, "Funny, I don't remember it being a full moon tonight."

CHAPTER 56

The panther had withdrawn into the hiding shadows of the tall grasses frustrated at missing out on a dinner of crow, but his continuing agitation was coming from something subtler. It was very unusual for a bird like that to be on its own so far from its nest at night. It wasn't feeding. It wasn't being chased. It was a strange thing indeed, but there was still something else. He circled back to where he had attacked the bird and, after determining it to be safe, he slinked up to the tail feathers he had knocked off of it. Leaning in close he gave them a sniff. The cold air and seed scent of the feathers, mixed with the dark, gamy smell of the smattering of crow's blood on the feather's tip came as no surprise, but the delicate undertone beneath of sweat and cotton… the boy! The crow had been with the boy!

The panther wheeled about and took off after Josiah like a shot into the night. This was the closest he had come yet to finding the boy and he was not about to let the chance slip through his claws again.

CHAPTER 57

A rmy felt very self-conscious standing over Wendy. If anyone came in or if she suddenly woke up he would look like some sort of thief in the night hovering over his victim. To try to make things look a little less threatening, he pulled Wendy's desk chair over to her bedside and sat down. He picked up a book from Wendy's desk. It was titled *What Your Dreams Mean*. He opened it up on his lap. He absurdly reasoned to himself that if someone came in, he would explain that he was doing a book report on this particular book but that he had left it at school; however, he knew Wendy had a copy and he needed to look something up before tomorrow's class. It was nuts, but he had to do something to make things look a little less awkward.

Thus situated, Army turned his attention to Wendy's closed eyes. Nothing. He put his hand on The Langdim Finder ready to make the jump. Wendy suddenly shifted a little in bed causing Army's heart to leap into his throat and his hand to grip The Langdim Finder harder, but then she became still once more. As Army's heart regained its normal place in his chest, he relaxed a bit and, in the silence of the room, under the glow of the moon, he suddenly realized how beautiful his friend looked and remembered how much he cared for her. He had become so wrapped up in everything that had been going on, and so determined to live up to his promise to save her from her dream, that he had lost sight of how it all began. That he simply really cared for her.

Then it happened. Wendy's eyes began to slowly move back and forth as if she were watching a movie being projected beneath her eyelids. She was starting to dream! Army's heart began to race once again. It was time for him to make the jump. He nervously took out The Langdim Finder, closed his eyes to concentrate and began to press the buttons while picturing The Wishing Well. Suddenly, Army opened his eyes again realizing that if he jumped then and there, his body would be left sleeping slumped in the chair. What if someone came in? What was he going to do? In his anguish, he fumbled The Langdim Finder and it fell to the floor. The good thing was that Wendy's bedroom had a wall-to-wall carpet, so The Finder hit noiselessly. The not-so-good thing was that it bounced under Wendy's bed. This was wasting time! Army hurriedly dove to the floor and slid himself under the bed to retrieve it.

"Wait a second," he thought to himself, "this is perfect. I'll jump from here and no one will find me!"

Army quickly resumed pressing The Finder's buttons while focusing his thoughts on The Wishing Well. The lights flickered with increasing rapidity and the next thing he knew, Army was back in Langdimania looking into the horrified eyes of Vladimir, Lucy, Gladys, and Jack.

CHAPTER 58

S he was floating again. Slowly rising towards a distant circle of light high above her head but this time she knew exactly where she was and what she was looking at. She breathed in the moist, earthy smell of The Wishing Well and felt oddly at ease. At least it was familiar this time and she was determined to break the spell that bound her to this bottomless tunnel.

Higher and higher Wendy floated, the circle of light now clearly coming into focus as the ever-present full moon. How was it always full?

"Because, as I told Army," Wendy said, answering her own thoughts, "this is a dream. And weird things happen in dreams," and then nonchalantly she added, "and the next weird thing will be the sound of conversation and oh, surprise, surprise, it'll turn out to be talking animals."

And sure enough, as Wendy neared the top of The Well, she began to hear voices in deep but rapid discussion.

"Hello!" Wendy shouted upwards, like she was calling up to a friend's window for them to come out to play, "Dream animals, I'm back!"

"It's her! It's her!" Jack cried out. "She's back!"

Vladimir stuck his head over the top of The Well wall and saw Wendy floating just a few meters out of his reach.

"Of course she is," he said to the animals behind him and out of Wendy's sight.

Suddenly, Josiah flew into view above Vladimir's head and screeched, "Not now! Not now!"

He flew down into the well, circling lower and lower until he could land on Wendy's shoulder and shouted at her, "Go away, go away! He's coming this way!"

Wendy's heart leapt, "Who's coming? Army? Army's here?"

"No!" Josiah yelled. "The beast! The giant beast!"

"Giant what?" Wendy gasped out loud and then she thought, "Has my dream become a nightmare again? Oh no, this just won't do. I wish this would stop!" And then she yelled directly at Josiah, "Make it stop!"

"Make it stop, she says. How? I'm just a crow!"

In the distance, the panther paused his chase after the bird. A human smell was back on the wind and coming from the direction the crow had flown to. This was it! His hunt was almost over! He gathered up his speed for a final run and raced towards The Well.

"This is just awful!" bleated Lucy.

Josiah came flapping up out of The Well.

"The girl is here, the monster is coming, where is Army?" he cried out.

"He'll be here," Vladimir replied sternly, and then repeated it again under his breath to himself. "He'll be here."

Jack was running around The Wishing Well sniffing the increasingly stiff wind excitedly. He came back to the others and exclaimed, "Whatever it is, it's coming in quick!"

Gladys reared up on her hind legs and whinnied, "He's here! He's here!"

Just then the moon blinked out of the sky along with the stars and then blinked back again, and then again and again with growing frequency. The panther, only a few seconds from The Well, stopped its attack and flattened to the ground. Peering out at the small clutch of animals, he watched intently as the lighting of the evening flickered to a climax and then went still and normal again. Normal, that is, except for the sudden appearance of the boy on top of the horse's bucking back.

"Army!" the animals all cried out.

Army had very little time to take in the scene before him while simultaneously grabbing tightly to Gladys's mane with one hand and shoving The Langdim Finder safely back into his pocket with the other.

"Vladimir, Lucy, Josiah! What's going on?" Army shouted to them above the wind. "Has Wendy arrived yet?"

Hearing him from just below the top of The Well, Wendy exclaimed, "Army? Army!"

"Wendy!"

Though his brain couldn't form the words, the panther understood that his quarry had finally returned and, even better, there were two of them now! One on the horse and one shouting from beneath the wall of stones. Silent beneath the roar of the rising squall, the wild cat coiled his powerful body into a spring ready to pounce and this time there would no escape for his victims.

Army jumped down from Gladys and was instantly surrounded by his friends.

"Oh, Army, it's so good to see you again!" cried Lucy.

"I always knew you'd come back, kid!" Josiah squawked.

Vladimir interrupted the reunion, "Not now, not now everybody! Army, you must rescue Wendy right this second. This is the moment, now!"

Understanding the gravity and the immediacy of Vladimir's words and tone, Army ran over to The Well, pulled himself up to the top of the wall and looked down. There was Wendy, floating just out of reach. His plan had worked; they were finally in Langdimania at the same time and in the same place!

"Wendy!" Army shouted down to her.

"Army!" Wendy shouted back. "Get me out of here!"

This was the moment Army had been working towards ever since he'd first heard of Wendy's arrival in Langdimania from Vladimir in the Tower so long ago. Long ago? How long ago? Time was too fuzzy for him to think about and he had a much more urgent problem at hand anyway. Exactly how was he to get her out of The Well? Like in a dream, nothing practical worked; ropes, pulling, or ladders. Everything that had been tried had already failed in the most ridiculous and strangest of ways.

"She's so close," Army thought to himself, "like I could just reach down and grab her."

And so he tried. Army simply leaned over the wall of The Well and extended his hand towards Wendy.

"It's no good, Army! You won't reach!" Wendy shouted up to him.

"Try, Wendy, just try!" Army shouted back, their voices echoing damply off the stones.

Wendy stretched her hand towards Army, but their fingers fell short of each other by just inches.

Josiah flew around them and cawed, "Hurry it up, Army. Jack says the monster cat is nearby!"

Panicking, Army yelled, "Hold on, Wendy, I'll get a boost!"

"No, Army, it won't work. I know this dream; anything you try to use will fall apart or fall down The Well!" Wendy started to cry and then said, "It's useless. I wish it was different, I wish I could reach you, but I can't."

Vladimir had joined Army looking over the wall and said to him, "Now, Army, you must act now."

Army was shaking with fear and frustration. He turned to Vladimir, tears now streaming down his face as well, and gasped, "Vladimir, help me, I don't know what to do. I thought I would know but I don't. I wish I knew; I wish I had the answer."

Vladimir looked back at Army, his blue eyes twinkling with kindness, wisdom, and ... was that a touch of sadness? "Now you listen to me, Army. I'm the chief professor of Patternology in all of Langdimania. I foresaw all of this and I know that you *do* have the answer. It's inside of you and it's not what you or I wish were true, but it's what we believe is true. And I believe in you, Army."

That was it! Wendy believed this was a dream and wished she could escape, but Army knew it wasn't a dream; he believed in Langdimania. He turned back towards Wendy and shouted to her, "Wendy! This isn't a dream. This is real. You have to believe me!"

Wendy looked back up at Army and saw the tears on his cheeks.

"I wish I could, Army, but I know this can't be real. It's all a dream and you're just a part of it."

"It's not about wishing, Wendy. It's about believing. And you have to believe me."

"But how can I? There's no proof, I can't prove Langdimania is real. I've tried grabbing pieces of the plants off of the wall of The Well so I'd wake up with them, but when I do awake, my hands are always empty!"

Army knew what that was like. One couldn't bring anything back from Langdimania. How could he make Wendy believe?

"Hurry, Army, hurry!" Josiah cawed.

Army's mind whirred with ideas but each one fell short of being a workable solution. He could try getting Wendy to wake up and find him under the bed, but with the fuzziness of time he wasn't sure if it would work, and with the panther about to attack he couldn't chance the consequences of a jump now.

Wait! He couldn't prove this was all real by bringing Wendy back to her room, but he could prove that he was in Wendy's room right now at the same time as being in Langdimania!

"Wendy! I've got the answer! In your bedroom, on your desk is a book called *What Your Dreams Mean*!"

"How... how do you know that?"

"Because I'm under your bed!"

"What?"

"I snuck into your room tonight so I could make the jump just as you started dreaming, and I saw the book on your desk!"

Wendy thought about this for a second, wanting desperately to believe, but then logic kicked in and she replied, "But Army, that doesn't prove anything. This is my dream so, if I dreamed you, I could just as well dream that you'd know what book was by my bed."

Army was stumped. He thought he had the answer. He looked at Vladimir in complete despair.

Vladimir spoke to him again with just one word, "Believe."

Army gathered his strength and turned to Wendy once more.

"Wendy, I don't know what else to do, I don't know what else to say other than that I am here to save you, just like you asked me to. Look, even if this is a dream of yours, it's your dream, you can control it, you can save yourself and all you have to do is believe me, believe in me, believe not in dreams but in yourself, decide what you want to happen and reach for my hand."

Army stretched his hand out as far as he could.

Then Wendy suddenly cried out, "To hell with this wishing well! I want to get out! I don't want to wish; I want to believe… I *DO* BELIEVE!"

Wendy stretched her hand back up to Army's and, with a final effort from both of them, their fingers touched, their hands clasped, and Army pulled Wendy out of The Wishing Well!

Once Wendy cleared the top, she continued to float, levitating for a few brief moments of freedom, laughing with happiness while holding Army's hand below her. Whether it was the gemstone clasped in her other hand or merely her joy at being liberated, Wendy cast a sparkling aura of shimmering golden light. With Army and the animals distracted by the beautiful vision, the panther saw his moment had arrived. Using his powerful hind leg muscles, he sprang into action, leaping forward and hitting the ground in a lightning-fast charge.

Things happened very quickly at that point. From her hovering height, Wendy was the first to sight the incoming attack and she let out a cry, "Look out!"

Josiah spotted the panther next and screamed, "Run away!"

Vladimir began to calculate as quickly as he could the right action to take, but Lucy, acting with her instinctual compassion, immediately put herself between the incoming danger and Army, while Jack ran forward to intercept the villain. But it was of no use; none of them were a match for the feline killing machine.

"Of course," Vladimir realized, "It was never Wendy who was destined to fall." And then he shouted in utter futility, "LUCY!"

The panther easily dodged the slower moving dog and continued his charge. Normally, a lamb dinner would have been impossible for him to pass up, but the beast had only one target in mind as he pounced upon Lucy as one would a trampoline, using her as a springboard toward his real goal.

As the alarm had gone up, Army turned and saw his old nemesis the panther hurtling towards him like a cannonball made from the night itself. His only thought was to protect Wendy, and he pulled her hand to bring her to the ground so that they could run, but she was stuck. While before he couldn't get her out of The Well, now he couldn't get her down from above it! She floated there; her face frozen in shock.

"Wendy!" Army cried, "He's going to eat me, let's go!"

But it was useless; she was too paralyzed with fear to be broken out of her spell. The panther pushed itself off Lucy with claws extended, slicing through the sheep as he continued his arc towards the kids. Lucy fell to the ground, bleating in pain and shock.

Suddenly, sensing its trajectory, Army realized that the panther wasn't gunning for him; it was Wendy he was after! Entranced by the glowing lights swirling about the girl, the panther had eschewed his original plan to get Army in favor of this glittering new prize. With less than a moment to spare, Army's love for Wendy activated his reflexes and he leaped toward her, pushing her out of harm's way and replacing himself as the target.

The panther and the boy collided and, for the briefest of nanoseconds, hung suspended like a grotesque mobile, before falling into the gaping mouth of the bottomless well.

CHAPTER 59

The midair collision of wild cat and boy knocked them both out, causing them to drop like wet sandbags flopping over one another into The Well. The rush of wind past their faces woke them both simultaneously. It's a strange thing to regain consciousness whilst plummeting into endless darkness. I believe that if one word best sums up the entire feeling then that word would be, "Yikes!"

"Yikes!" Army yelled.

"Yikes!" the panther repeated loudly, as they both hung onto each other in vain attempts to stop the fall.

I believe the one word that best describes the realization that you are not only falling, but are falling with a wild panther that wants to eat you is, "Yaaaaargh!"

"Yaaaaargh!" Army screamed as he tried to disentangle himself from the clutches of the beast.

This just caused the panther to grip Army tighter as the circle of light above them grew rapidly smaller and further away.

"Let me go! Let me go!" Army commanded.

"Hold on! Hold on!" the panicking panther yelled back.

Army shut his eyes in anxious preparation for his inevitable crash to the ground. A few seconds that seemed like an eternity passed by and, as no murderous introduction with the ground occurred, Army slowly opened one eye and then both. He was in complete darkness, except for the unnerving green glow of the panther's eyes.

"Wait, you can talk again!" Army realized out loud to his freefalling companion.

"What?" cried the cat.

"You can talk!"

"Yes, I can," the panther said, licking his lips, "and now I've finally got you!"

Army felt the beast tense up to strike.

"Wait!" Army cried out.

"Why?"

"We're falling down The Well!"

"So we are, and if this is to be my last meal before we hit the bottom, then at least it'll be a fine one!"

"But we won't hit bottom; The Well is bottomless!"

The panther considered this for a moment and then said, "It doesn't matter. You're prey and I'll eat you."

The initial rush of wind that accompanied their falling into The Well had subsided and there was an almost eerie stillness to their descent now. Army no longer had to shout. He steadied his voice and, as calmly as he could, he explained, "If you eat me, I'll be gone."

"So? My stomach will be full!"

"Yes, but for how long? Soon, you'll be hungry again and there'll be no prey. Just you. Alone. Falling in the dark forever with no one to talk to."

The panther pondered this, now that he was able to ponder, and the thought made him oddly uncomfortable.

"But catching and eating prey is what I do," he said, a bit uncertainly.

Army, the expert in getting out of tight situations, saw his opening.

"You hesitated! You don't like the idea of falling forever alone."

"No, but I like the idea of starving even less!"

Army quickly pressed his advantage.

"But maybe it doesn't have to be this way. That feeling you felt about being scared…"

"I'm not scared!" roared the giant cat, hurting Army's ears.

"Not scared! No, certainly not! Who's scared? Not you!" Army said, trying to cool the conversation back down. "I meant that feeling of being alone, of having thoughts with nobody to tell them to. That's a different kind of hunger, of emptiness."

"I've always been alone," the panther said. "The emptiness keeps me going, keeps me hunting."

"Yes, but every time you kill one animal, another one somewhere has lost their one to talk with and the emptiness just spreads, it gets bigger. If you kill and eat me now you'll be full, but soon after that you'll be empty again and not just in your belly but all over. It's how I felt when my brother Nick started ignoring me and hid in a room as dark as this stupid well, or when my best friend Mike walked away from me when I couldn't hang out with him in school, and worst of all when Wendy didn't appear with me when I first tried to jump with her here to Langdimania. That sudden aloneness is the worst feeling I ever had, worse and ever so much emptier than hunger!"

"If I eat you, it will make me emptier?" the panther said, half to Army and half to himself. Army felt as if he was watching the panther becoming enlightened before his eyes.

But suddenly, the panther shook his head violently back and forth, as if trying to eject these strange thoughts from his mind, and roared, "No! I don't know this Nick, Mike, or Wendy, they mean nothing to me and I'm hungry NOW!"

The great monster opened his fanged mouth wide, his hot savage breath inches from Army's face, forcing Army to realize that just telling the panther about loneliness could never be as powerful as showing him. There was only one solution, and so Army wriggled out of his sweatshirt, pushed away from the great cat, and allowed himself to plummet further ahead into the darkness.

"NO!" bellowed the beast, horrified at the loss of his dinner.

And so they fell, with Army only several feet ahead of the panther; but in the blackness he might as well have been miles away.

"Boy, where are you?" cried the panther over and over for what felt like an eternity, his plaintive cries growing softer and softer until eventually all that Army could hear was the sobbing of the terrified animal. Army waited a while longer and then spoke up, "So, how's it feel to be alone?"

If he had been on the ground, the panther would have jumped high into the air at Army's sudden question; but as he was already in the air it looked more like he had just had an electric shock.

"You're still alive?" he cried out.

"Yes," Army replied, and then continued cautiously, "do you still want to eat me?"

"No!" the panther exclaimed. "No, you were right, the loneliness is torture! I thought I was going to be all alone falling in the dark forever! Please stay with me, I won't eat you, just don't leave me alone!"

"Now you're getting it! You're understanding it!" Army cheered.

And then Army realized that they didn't seem to be falling anymore, but rather they were floating in place and Army had risen to come face to face with the panther once again.

"Do other creatures ever feel this way?" The panther asked.

"Yes, all of them, but the animals of F'orest can't express it; they don't have language yet like you do now."

A great sorrow passed over the panther as he recalled his long history of hunting, of killing, of causing others to feel the loneliness he had just experienced. And as these recollections, these overwhelming feelings of regret sank upon him, they began falling once again, and The Well seemed darker than ever.

"It's awful," cried the panther. "I've harmed so many. I've brought the emptiness to so many!"

Faster and faster they began to fall until Army feared they'd never stop; they'd never get out!

"No, panther! It wasn't your fault. You didn't know any better. You didn't have the reasoning, you hadn't the… the… illumination yet! You can still do good. You can make up for it."

"How?"

Army thought about all the bad things he himself had done, like making his classmates into servants to try to win

Wendy's approval, and how only her forgiveness, her belief in him, had relieved him of the guilt.

"Forgiveness, panther. I forgive you for attacking me. I know it was just your nature and you didn't know any better. But now you do, and I believe that you'll do good from now on."

"I will! I will!" the panther bellowed, and their descent slowed down until they were once again merely floating in place.

"And now comes the hardest part; you have to forgive yourself."

"How do I do that?"

"Just do it. It may feel silly at first but just say it out loud. That's what words are for!"

The panther took a deep breath and thought about his life thus far. A life that had brought pain and misery to so many. A life that lead him to this moment of being trapped in the dark, filled with a terrible emptiness and desperation. A life he was ready to leave behind.

"I wish to stop the emptiness, the sorrow, the grief," the panther said.

Nothing happened, they simply continued to float in place.

"Don't wish for it," Army said, "Believe it. Believe that you are forgiven. For I forgive you, panther, but you have to, too."

"I... I... I forgive myself," the panther whispered softly.

Gently, they began to rise.

"That's it! That's it! It's working. Keep going, say it louder."

"I forgive myself," the panther said, more confidently.

They were definitely rising now.

Army joined in, "I forgive myself for not reaching out better to Nick and Mike and I'll make it up to them if I can just get out of here!"

Not to be outdone the panther continued, "I'll atone for what I've done. I'll ask forgiveness from all I've harmed and spend the rest of my days helping rather than harming my fellow creatures!"

That did it. They were now rising rapidly as if they were standing on top of an express elevator. The darkness around them turning into dusky greys and dark blues and then lighter blues as the halo of light and sky above their heads grew larger and brighter, and then seconds later they shot out of The Wishing Well and landed tumbling in the wet grass of the new morning.

CHAPTER 60

L ucy lay deathly still in the grass; the other animals gathered around her with bowed heads. Deep red streaks on her back and side revealed where the panther had clawed her as he used her to mount his attack on the human children. Wendy was by Lucy's side, tending to her even though her tears for Army, now lost to The Well and the panther's attack, fogged her vision.

Josiah had flown at top speed to alert the other animals of F'arm to the horrible events that had occurred, and many of them had already arrived to help. Some of Jack's pack had brought fresh water in big shells from the river to wash Lucy's wounds and Oscar, an old and wise rabbit, had applied antibacterial bandage patches made from woven plantain leaves.

As the moon sank towards the horizon, more and more animals of F'arm arrived, until eventually almost all of them had returned.

Gladys watched over the proceedings, anxiously pacing back and forth from the stricken sheep to The Well. On her most recent check-in with Vladimir she asked once again, "Anything?"

Vladimir just sadly shook his head 'no' and Gladys persisted, "And Lucy? Will she…" Gladys couldn't bring herself to finish her sentence but everyone knew what she meant.

"This is so sad," a squirrel fretted, "when we were all last here, we had such high hopes for the boy to rescue The Girl and usher in the new dawn, but we never thought it'd mean that Lucy would be sacrificed to do it!"

"Vladimir," a skylark twittered, "how could you not have foreseen such a tragic outcome?"

"Yes, and if you did know, Vladimir, why didn't you stop it?" a badger joined in.

"What's the use of knowing the universal will if you can't stop tragedies like this?" the skylark insisted.

Vladimir stood up and faced the gathered animals. There were no easy answers to their questions, but he knew that he had to say something to help them move through this terrible moment. He cleared his throat and began, "I too have wondered at times what the point of it all is. However, time and again I see that it *is* worthwhile, that the great patterns include the awful pain of loss, but they also embrace the joyous pain of birth. That happiness and sadness are intertwined and what seems unthinkably horrible one moment can produce something incredibly wonderful the next. I don't know why, but I know it happens, and in understanding and accepting the patterns we can find a sense of peace. No pattern is permanent but rather they are ever-changing, and faith, acceptance, and understanding are the tools we use to weather the changes in the patterns, the mysterious ways things end up working out.

"Yes, I foresaw that the boy would rescue the girl, but I didn't see the terrible cost that would entail, or perhaps my own ego blinded me to it. Perhaps I was so set on being right that I didn't take in to account the timing of the beast's attack."

The crowd was silent. They had never experienced this kind of humility from Vladimir before. They were used to him boasting of "always being right", not to him admitting that wanting to be so could be the cause of his own ignorance!

"So, it's hopeless then," a small mouse child squeaked.

Her mother shushed the little girl and motioned toward Wendy sitting sorrowfully just a few feet away, but it was too late, Wendy had heard her and started crying again.

"Now, see what you've done," the mother mouse admonished her daughter, who looked dreadfully sorry that she had said anything. But then the strangest thing happened; Wendy started laughing.

"Wendy?" Josiah said, "Are you OK?" He thought the poor girl was going crazy with grief.

"Don't you see?" Wendy said, standing up and holding her gemstone high above her head. She looked radiant as the sun began to rise behind her and the jewel cast glittering colors across her tear-stained face. "It's *never* hopeless. It's like Vladimir said; each moment contains the seeds of the next one. From bad to good to bad to good. And it is acceptance and faith or, as Army called it, 'belief', that are the keys to getting through it all."

And then Wendy raised her voice to the skies and proclaimed, "I accept the loss of my friend who saved me and I have faith, I believe like he taught me to, that miracles happen all the time, from falling rain to a nest of eggs, from rabbits that are doctors to animals that can talk, for gosh sakes! And that more such wonders will sprout from the dark soil of this awful night!"

And then, as if on cue, Army and the panther came hurtling out of The Wishing Well and crashed to the ground right at Wendy's feet.

CHAPTER 61

H ave you ever heard an entire field of animals gasp in unison? Probably not. How about at a sporting event when a player unexpectedly gets injured and the whole stadium holds their breath to see if he or she is okay? Yes? Well, that is what it sounded like when Army and the panther suddenly popped out of The Well and lay collapsed in the grass amongst them.

"I can't believe it!" Josiah was the first to respond.

Army and the panther disentangled themselves from each other and stood up.

"But I can! Army!" Wendy exclaimed, and ran over to him.

Jack jumped in front of her and said, "Hold on, my lady, that's the beast with Army, it's not safe."

Army and his new friend looked around and took in the sight of the animals gathered under the morning sun. Army immediately sensed the sorrow the panther felt at the fear he engendered from the gathering.

"Wendy!" Army exclaimed, walking toward her with the panther by his side. "Everybody! It's OK. The panther helped save me!"

"No, you saved me," the panther added solemnly.

"Well, then," Army continued as the two approached Wendy and the others, "we both saved each other. He can talk now, he can reason, and he no longer wishes to…"

And then Army and the giant cat stopped in their tracks, for they had come upon the gravely wounded Lucy.

"Reason now, can he?" Oscar the rabbit yelled at them. "Well, what's his reason for doing this to poor Lucy!" He pointed to the awful injuries that the cat had inflicted on the stricken sheep.

The panther wanted to run. Everything about this was foreign to him; being in the open, in the light. He sensed the smell of the dying around Lucy, her ears limp, her eyes shut, and then he woefully looked at Army, who simply said, "Just say what's in your heart; just tell the truth."

"You want the truth? OK, here's the truth," the panther said, with the kind of anger only true sorrow can unveil. "When I'm on a hunt, all I care about is the hunt! Getting my prey, filling my empty belly. The sheep was in my way and so I used her to get to the girl who filled my eyes with a prize no hunter could resist!"

The animals hadn't expected such a brutal confession, and they backed away from the now snarling beast in sheer terror, whispering to each other, "He's a monster" and, "He'll kill us all".

Army came forward, "He's not a monster, he's an animal. Just like all of us! Which one of you doesn't feel the empty belly every day?"

"But we don't eat each other, Army," Gladys whispered harshly.

"Don't you? Some of you eat insects, don't you? And worms, and frogs, and fish?"

"But they aren't smart animals, they don't reason like us," an otter, who was especially fond of fish dinners, said.

"They may not talk, but they may have feelings like you did before you were affected by the gem."

"But I don't eat any animal," Gladys said proudly. "I just eat grass and hay, and I certainly never hurt anyone the way he did poor Lucy."

"But what about the insects caught up in the grass you eat? Or the ones you trample upon unknowingly as you graze?" Army countered.

"But we have to eat, Army, or we'd die," said a hedgehog named Ralph.

"And so must the panther."

A confused and unsettling silence filled the field as each animal calculated their place and responsibility in the food chain.

Finally, Vladimir spoke up, "Yes, we must eat. It is the pattern of life, but now, in this moment, something has changed, hasn't it?"

"How about the humans?" enquired the ever-challenging sparrow, Lily. "What do they eat?"

Wendy and Army looked out over the faces of the animals before them and thought of all the hamburgers, hotdogs, chickens, and lamb chops they had enjoyed over the years, and then, together, they both said, "Salads."

The panther spoke again, but this time directly to the fallen Lucy who lay so limp upon the ground wet with her blood, "I'm sorry. You weren't my prey, but caught up in my pursuit I harmed you anyway. My fall in The Well with the boy showed me an emptiness far worse than hunger. The emptiness of loneliness, despair, regret, and fear. I am who I am and I can't change the way I was made, but I can change how I manage myself. I'm so sorry."

And then, ever so slowly, Lucy's eyes fluttered open to look up at the panther, whose own eyes were filled with tears, and she thought, "This is it. This is the moment."

Lucy turned her gaze to Vladimir who nodded to her in assent, his face filled with a mixture of ancient wisdom and childlike wonder. She understood and turned back to what, before, had been her biggest fear, but now was her greatest opportunity: this giant cat. With that realization, she felt a new vitality take hold of her and she said to him, "We were who we were, but now we are who we are, and I forgive you. So, take that silly look off your face and lie down beside me." Lucy then gave the onlooking crowd her well-known smile and uncharacteristically shouted, "And can someone please bring us a pot of tea!"

"She's going to be OK!" Army exclaimed so loudly that he fell backwards onto the grass with Wendy laughing beside him. The animals cheered riotously, breaking out into little dances with each other, and hugging one another while exulting Lucy's recovery. The panther grinned broadly and lay down next to her as a call was transferred across the field telling of the reconciliation, and the request for a decent cup of tea.

CHAPTER 62

A nd so it was that Carl, for that was the name the panther had decided on for himself, and Lucy enjoyed a cup of black peppermint tea under the midday sun. The news of Wendy's rescue and Carl's redemption spread far and wide across F'arm, as did the debate over what they were all to eat from now on. Many a belly groaned at the thought of giving up fish dinners or fat wormy breakfasts.

Eventually, Carl knew it was time for him to return to F'orest, as Army and Wendy both knew it was time for them to return to their homes too, even though no consensus had been arrived at over the whole eating thing.

Finally, Vladimir arose, held his big, black hoof high above his head and called for quiet.

"My friends, and I'm humbled and honored to call you such, I've pondered this question of what to do about our eating habits now that we've all been made aware of how each of our diets affects others, and I've come to the simple conclusion that this is a choice that each and every one of us has to make individually. We each have to decide for ourselves where we want to go from here. An overriding pattern in life is that actions have consequences and, with our ability to reason, we must take responsibility for our actions. I don't have a solution that will fit for all of you but I, for one, will limit my diet to the fruits and vegetables of F'arm."

"And I will be more careful where I step," said Gladys.

"Well, until one of them sits up and introduces themselves to me, I'm still having worms for breakfast!" countered Josiah.

"And fish for lunch!" cried Ralph.

And then the animals all began talking at once over what they would and wouldn't eat going forward. Sensing it was time for him to depart, Carl arose and said to Vladimir, Lucy, and the children, "Thank-you for accepting me, but I must get back to F'orest now; my place is there."

"Will you still hunt?" Army asked cautiously.

Carl paused and looked out at the arguing animals of F'arm. He gave a wink to Vladimir and said, "I'll think about it." And then he began his run back home.

Army turned to Wendy and said, "I think it's time for us to go as well."

"Yes, Army," Wendy said. "Let's go home."

The boy and girl raised their charms above their heads, the sun gleaming off of Wendy's gemstone as Army began pushing the buttons on his Langdim Finder.

"Goodbye everyone!" they shouted, as the light flickered between day and night.

The animals stopped their bickering and turned to face the vanishing boy and girl.

They shouted for them to stay, to help them decide what to do, to lead them.

"You don't need us. Listen to Vladimir, learn the patterns for yourselves, believe in the changes you want to happen, and don't worry, we'll be back!"

And then, they were gone.

CHAPTER 63

Army woke up in the dark, lifted his head, and whacked it against the slats of Wendy's bed. "Ow!" he cried out.

"Ow?" Wendy thought to herself as she awoke, and then out loud she said, "Who said that?"

Army moaned from under her bed. "Who do you think said it? It's me. I just hit my head!"

Army slid out into the open to see Wendy's delighted face.

"It wasn't a dream! I'm out of The Well! Lucy's OK! It's all real!" she shouted with glee, grabbing Army and dancing around her room with him.

From the hallway, Wendy's father's voice bellowed, "Wendy, go to sleep!"

"Oops," Wendy said, and she and Army froze in place with goofy smiles on their faces.

Army whispered, "I better get out of here."

"Yes, you better."

Army headed to the still open window of Wendy's bedroom and she whispered after him, "I'll see you at school tomorrow?"

Army answered with a smile as he climbed out and onto the roof, "Yes, and I think I've finally got an idea for the musical Mr Fulmar wants me to write."

Wendy looked out of the window and said, "Does it have anything to do with talking pigs?"

Army just said, "Well…"

And they both laughed as he dropped down over the side and ran down the street to his home on Cherry Lane.

"I wonder what will happen next …"

Lach, pronounced "Latch".

Printed in Great Britain
by Amazon

18040784R00132